The Novello Book of Carols

The Novello
Book of Carols

compiled and edited by
William Llewellyn

Novello
London and Sevenoaks

to my family
and in our affectionate remembrance of
Warren Green

A M D G

Registered office, trade orders, and hire library:
Borough Green, Sevenoaks, Kent, TN15 8DT tel: 0732 883261
Showroom, editorial, retail sales, and mail order:
8 Lower James Street, London, W1R 4DN tel: 01-734 8080

Part One Cat. No. 05 0046 ISBN 0 85360 125 9

Part Two Cat. No. 05 0047 ISBN 0 85360 126 7

Complete Cat. No. 05 0048 ISBN 0 85360 127 5

Cover illustration *I Re Magi* (S. Apollinare Nuovo, Ravenna)
© Scala/Firenze Reproduced by permission

Cover design by Malcolm Harvey Young FSIAD, MSTD

Contents

Introduction

When I was invited to produce suggestions for a comprehensive new Christmas carol collection, I was delighted to be able to draw on over 35 years' experience of organizing and directing Carol Concerts and Services. Having had to produce many arrangements of my own to suit many varied choral and instrumental demands – both amateur and professional – my initial file of ideas grew rapidly and this Novello Book of 90 Carols is the result.

16 carols and a further 39 arrangements are published here for the first time.

Carols from France, Holland, Germany, Italy, Czechoslovakia, and Canada, are included, and the three carols from Spain I obtained from Snr Enrique Ribo following a concert tour to Barcelona with the Linden Singers. Three of my own arrangements were written in Italy, and a visit to Ravenna inspired the idea for the cover illustration.

69 carols are suitable for unaccompanied singing; the Index shows this. Further, it is often useful to have readily available alternative settings – in mood, style, length, or scoring – of the same words, and 14 of these are included. The provision of Performing Notes is indicated by *PN* at the head of the music where applicable.

The book runs mainly in alphabetical order under first lines of English text, but we have made a few changes to try to keep repeated sections on facing pages and to avoid awkward turns forward or back.

Orchestral parts and full scores for 24 of the carols are obtainable on hire; details of the orchestrations, and much other useful information, will be found in the comprehensive Index at the end.

This Novello Book of Carols (NBC) is also the parent book for The Novello Junior Book of Carols (NJBC) which contains 21 pieces from it. The arrangements, all compatible with NBC, have Chime Bars, School Percussion, two Melody Parts (each in C & B flat), Guitar chords, Bass Line, and simplified Piano. They make possible joint Concerts and Services with Schools and Adult Choirs; the full orchestral scores include all the school parts.

I am most grateful to all musical contributors: to James Woodhouse, Headmaster of Lancing College, for his skill in finding words which create so successfully atmosphere, sound, and meaning: to my colleague, Robin Totton, for his help with the Catalan texts: and especially to Robin Langley, Publisher to Novello & Company, for his acute perception and for his untiring interest and industry; without him, and Leslie Ellis with the expert team of technical staff, this book would never have come into being.

Charterhouse, 1986 *William Llewellyn*

Performing Notes

The carols are listed alphabetically under first lines

NO. PAGE

1 1 }
2 2 } *A babe is born.* Each version lilts gently, with a considerable dynamic range overall, and some freedom in the unison refrains. With four voices only, omit Alto 1 and Bass 1 in the last few bars of each version.

4 6 *A little child there is yborn.* This should be taken at a steady pace so that all the quavers can be articulated – they should be crisp and detached, not smooth. It will go very well at ♩.= 92, but could be sung faster, up to ♩.= 104.

6 14 *Ancient prophets first foretold him.* This is undoubtedly a March, and the men should sound like a brass band; a good 'm' at the end of each 'Fum' will help to make the effect. The upper voices are also part of the marching procession – perhaps as children running and dancing round the band as it marches through the streets.

5 9 *As I walked down the road.* The humming accompaniment moves serenely throughout the opening. The word 'Star' (bar 26) can form a real climax, and can be matched in exhilaration by the word 'shining'.

10 22 *As Joseph was a-walking*. Serene and dignified. Verses 2 and 4 may have different soloists. The 'Mm' may have half-closed lips if this suits the acoustics.

7 16 *Away in a manger*. Even-sounding throughout, with no *crescendi* or *rallentandi* to disturb the gentle flow, and with no hint of pauses between verses. In contrast to this, the final humming surges and grows, before receding to the very soft finish.

8 18 *Blessed be he that cometh*. The 'Ah' at the beginning of each section starts confidently and then 'makes room' for the hints of plainsong which it supports. The rhythmic pulse of the Refrain makes a good contrast.

75 229 *Born in the night*. The words tell you precisely the expression needed. The layout here is explained under carol 74, p.viii, 'The First Nowell'. 'Born in the night' also sounds well between verses of 'Hark! the herald angels sing' – use two verses of 'Born in the night' each time; either transpose the carol down (to F), or up (to A flat).

9 20 *Christmas is coming*. This can have real outdoor carol style. Walford Davies once explained that in bars 5 and 6 ('hat____') the old man is poking his hat at the passers-by. There is a chance of a spectacular *crescendo* at the end of bar 13. The traditional tune at the end will take a rustic, almost clumsy, treatment with the quavers heavier than usual. And the final unison E flat can really ring.

14 30 *De Virgin Mary had a baby boy*. Plenty of West Indian swing, and a sense of good humour can emerge. 'Duh', not 'Dee'. The dynamic contrasts should be large.

13 29 *Ding-dong, ding*. There is an alternative 'Rondo Route' through this carol and it balances well. Sing straight through the whole page with only the first set of words; straight through again, but with the second set of words; finish with the opening line. The words ''tis no fable' sound well sung very softly, as a one-bar aside.

15 34 *Ding dong! merrily on high (i)*. To avoid the usual trap of 'Hosanna-rin excelsis' I asked the choir to add a rest, and the 5/4 time seemed to follow naturally.

17 37 *Donkey plod and Mary ride*. This is adapted from Eric Thiman's unison song, 'The Path to the Moon'. The carol-like quality of the tune made me look for suitable words; these by Timothy Dudley-Smith might easily have been written specially for this tune.

19 44 *Dormi Jesu. (ii)*. Very calm and serene, with a feeling of a tune in each of the three parts: the cadences all have major triads and there is an opportunity for beautiful, glowing chords.

22 50 *God rest you merry, gentlemen*. This should be full of *bonhomie* and energy. The last few bars should be taken by storm.

20 46 *Hark, the herald angels sing*. Mendelssohn's 'Festgesang' (scored for male chorus and brass, and originally having no connection with Christmas) supplies the opening fanfare. The barring is his also.

21 49 *Hodie, hodie Christus natus est*. This can make an excellent start for a Carol Service or Concert. There are two possible endings to suit the keys of the carol or hymn following.

23 57 *How soft, upon the ev'ning air*. Many pieces of music have one bar or one section which suggests the speed appropriate for the whole. Here it is the bar of 'See how he sleeps'; this has a hint of both repose and movement. If this bar is at the right speed for the acoustic of the place in which you are singing, the whole will sound good.

24 60 *Hushaby low*. The chorus should be very restrained throughout, and particularly when accompanying the soprano at the beginning. Here the solo voice should be thrown into relief as though the Madonna were illuminated by a single candle in a darkened room.

25 63 *Hush you, my baby*. At bar 69 the plural word SOLOISTS asks for a soprano voice and a man's voice together. You could use more than one of each voice, but each octave should be there. It would be possible to sing the whole carol to the music of verse 2.

26 66 *I'm a-ridin' to Bethlehem*. The trotting horse ('Troc-a-tron') approaches, goes past, and away, all in a few seconds. The hard 'c' clicks in each bar, the quaver (-a-) has its own energy and the 'n' of 'tron' must be heard clearly. Though the tune comes from Czechoslovakia, you may like to try a touch of mid-Western accent. At the end of the piece no hint of slowing, but simply sounding further away until out of earshot. Your own tempo will depend on the two words 'trot quickly' and how well they sound in your acoustic.

29 76 *In the bleak mid-winter (i)*. This may be sung very thoughtfully: in verse 3 (. . .'thronged the air'), the heavenly celebrations should be very loud; the singers then sing very softly without any break so that the next words 'but only his mother' are 'discovered' as the loud phrase dies away.

30 80 *In the bleak mid-winter (ii)*. Verse 3 can be very effective with solo soprano accompanied by humming choir. The parts for strings and wind can be used as interludes between the sung verses.

28a 72 }
28b 74 } *In this most joyful night*. This arrangement of a most evocative tune is never loud – the intensity of the notes is carried up to the ends of phrases more than in our own English tradition; this brings out the elusive quality of the song.

31 81 *In thy mother's arms*. I found this lullaby in Rome and have used it frequently. The soloist sings gently above the rocking accompaniment. A little extra weight in the last bar (C flat) for the choir will help the finish, but the general mood never changes.

33 86 *I saw three ships (ii)*. When John Wilson asked me to make an arrangement of this I asked, 'Which of the two well-known tunes shall I use?' His answer was 'Both!' It is quite easy to run the two different tunes at your own chosen speeds; the last few bars should be quite fast and almost 'thrown away', with the speed maintained to the final bar.

34 89 *I sing of a maiden*. Serene, using the simple resonances of the chords. With four voices only, omit Bass 1 in bars 10 and 10a.

35 90 *Jerusalem rejos for joy*. There is a great deal of atmosphere here with majesty and mystery combined, and possibilities of rich texture and colouring. 'Ch' is pronounced as in Scottish 'loch'; 'Jerusalem' and 'josit' each have a hard 'j'.

38 99 *Joy to the world (ii)*. There is so much of Handel's character in this strong tune that it seemed natural to clothe the three verses with Handelian accompaniments and interludes. There are some easily-recognisable quotations in the added parts.

39 104 *King Jesus hath a garden*. Always gentle and soothing; the hints of flutes and other instruments are obvious but always miniature. This garden is sunny and contains a great variety of colour.

43 116 *Lully, lulla (ii)*. In this arrangement the refrain comes only at the beginning and at the end. As well as the 3/4 time there are sections which should be sung as if they are in 3/2 and 6/8. The 6/8 in particular should be strongly rhythmical.

45 120 *Mary's Child, so new and fair*. The contraltos rock the cradle all the time. There is an echo, shown by the figures I and II, implicit in the tune (and in James Woodhouse's words). You may obtain this echo effect by distance or you may create it from within the choir. There is a real climax, but the piece is always intimate, starting almost imperceptibly and fading away to nothing at the end.

44a 118 }
44b 119 } *Mary, Mother of God's dear child*. Very busy and energetic. The accents on 'Oh' in contralto, tenor, and bass can be featured. Verse 3 can be extremely quiet, with a real contrast when the *ff* final verse comes. In Spain they sing the last few bars so loudly and triumphantly that you forget your fears about waking the baby.

50 140 *Nowell, Nowell, Who is there?* Plenty of accent and robust quavers all through both the refrains and the tune sections; the final 'Nowell' should be flung out as a challenge.

53 156 *Now is Christemas ycome*. Sing buoyantly with much rhythmic verve. The repeated chords (as in bar 7) should be very full, but also clear and precise. The quavers after the ties (e.g. 'fere' in bar 10) have no length, and so the final consonant comes on the beat.

55 164 *O come, all ye faithful*. If you do not wish to sing verse 6 ('born this happy morning') you can use the setting of it for any other verse (though you will probably wish to make it your final one).

57 170 *O magnum misterium*. Each 'choir' can be replaced by an organ or by an accompanying group. Parts are available on hire for brass instruments. The characteristic richness of the writing will still be heard. The triple-time 'Alleluia' should sound very lively and buoyant.

59 184 *Once in royal David's city*. The traditional treatment of the opening verse as a solo may, of course, be adopted. For unaccompanied use, the words of verse 6 may be sung to the A.H. Mann setting on the opposite page.

60 186 *O my dear heart (ii)*. A third verse, hummed *pp*, helps to carry the carol's special serenity.

62 195 *Past three o'clock (ii)*. This may be performed in two different ways: you may sing the whole piece, or simply bars 32-120. This arrangement is a reminder that these are the London Waits, with the watchman calling the time as the clock chimes – no-one heeds him; and the next section is slow, with distant carol singers approaching. At bar 32 the singers have arrived; keep this part bright and lively, bringing out each carol tune as it comes. In the 'Good King Wenceslas' section, one (at most two) baritones sing first bass. Their voices should be heard only as a means of deepening and thickening the tenor-bass sound. An off-stage horn where marked (a hint of 'Die Meistersinger'?) can be effective. The horn player plays from the vocal score at concert pitch.

The dynamic range of a real bell is huge – a loud clang, dying away very rapidly, turning slowly into a humming sound which slowly dies away. A hard 'D' on the 'Don' will help; and you may get different bell timbres by inviting various 'bell-singers' to use a different vowel sound (French 'Din' is an example'). The final bell-sound goes on for a long time and you can let it fade into the surrounding resonance.

65 204 *Rejoice lordings*. This should be sung with a great deal of word-energy, and in a very direct manner from beginning to end. The last bars give no hint that you are ending and should take the listener by surprise.

66 209 *See him born*. Think of a Gavotte, with firm accents on the first of the bar, and the piece will dance. Sing 'le diveen-enfant'. The humming should be nasal, buzzing, to imitate the sound and drone of pipes or French hurdy-gurdy.

67 212 }
68 213 } *See, to us a child is born*. The antiphon effect can be obtained by using two groups, one singing the words in roman type, the other those in italics.

71 220 *Sweet was the song the Virgin sang*. Each of the three 'La-lu-la' sections is more expansive than the one before; the time-signatures indicate this.

72 223 *The angel Gabriel*. This arrangement dances just a little. It may be sung unaccompanied by ignoring the interludes and lengthening the last chord in verses 1-3.

74 228 *The first Nowell*. The descants are optional and can be used in any verse. The second descant (verse 4 onwards), with its cross-rhythm, is the more energetic in style.

To make a real finish to a Carol Service it is always possible to 'sandwich' one carol inside another. 'Born in the night' sung during 'The First Nowell' is a good example and it is printed here so that you may sing either carol separately, or follow the order of the printed pages. The opening of the unaccompanied verses must be carefully rehearsed.

If a congregation is to join in singing the special setting of the last verse, a congregational rehearsal will obviously be desirable.

76 234 *The holly and the ivy*. The solo voice may be a treble or a tenor, each singing in alternate verses. The organ may play with the choir, but it must play its own part in bars 12-15. A second group of singers, or congregation, may sing the tune of the refrain.

78 238 *There is no rose of such virtue*. There are opportunities here for matching the parts when singing together or in canon, with a beautiful and serene ending.

84 256 *Tyrle, tyrlow*. These words are pronounced as if made up of three syllables and split to sound 'ty-re-leh, ty-re-low'. The musical rhythm throughout must be

86 264 *Villagers all, this frosty tide*. This is the Carol of the Field-Mice, and a reading from Kenneth Grahame's 'The Wind in the Willows' makes a good introduction.

83 253 *What shall we give?* The speed should be set so that the semi-quavers receive considerable weight and become almost heavy. This is not a rocking carol. In the last verse the unusual long-held F sharp should be insistent until finally it becomes part of the last chord; the voices singing 'non' should do so emphatically and with intensity.

88 270 *Worship the Christ-child*. The three choirs may be three quartets and the canon will sound well if the groups are spaced apart. The organisation is very simple; each choir enters as soon as the previous one reaches the asterisk. Thus each choir sings through each verse once (the same music three times) and then adds the short Coda (here called 'Verse 4'). Performed in this way, Choir 1 begins alone for the first bar-and-a-half and Choir 3 finds itself singing the Coda alone at the finish. There is an obvious climax in the middle.

1. A BABE IS BORN (i)

2. A BABE IS BORN (ii)

Words traditional
English 15th century

ROBIN WELLS

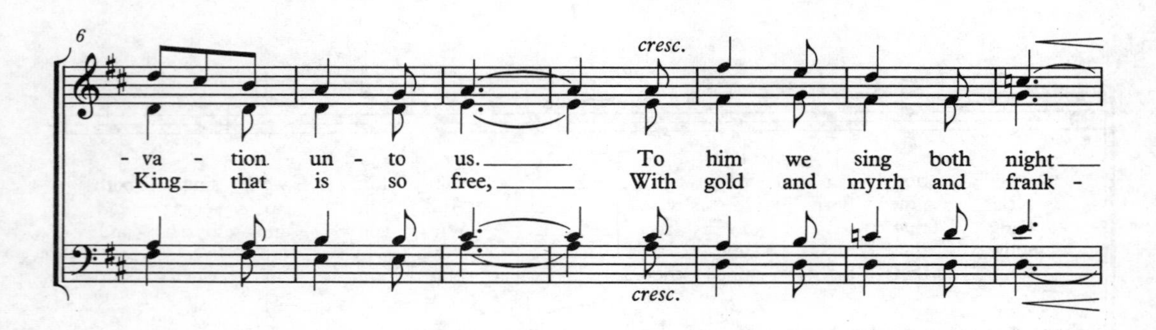

* maid

born he was; And him to serve God give us
night sung he. 'O why are ye so sore -
grace, O lux be - a - ta Tri - ni - tas.
- ghast ?' Jam or - tus so - lis car - di - ne. 5. The an - gels came down
with one cry, A fair song that night sung they
To
join in wor - ship of that child:
Glo - ri - a
To join in wor - ship of that child:
Glo - ri - a ti - bi Do - mi - ne.
ti - bi Do - mi - ne. Mm, mm.

3. ADAM LAY YBOUNDEN

Words anon. 15th century

BORIS ORD

17
FULL
mf
3. Ne had the ap - ple tak - en been, The ap - ple tak - en been,
mf FULL
21
cresc.
Ne had nev - er our lа - dy A - been hea - ven - é queen.
cresc.
25
f legato
4. Bless - ed be the time That ap - ple tak - en was,
f legato
29
gra - - - - - - ci -
There - fore we moun* sing - en, De - o gra - - - ci - as, De - o
gra - - - - - - ci -
33
- as, De - o gra - - - - ci - - as!
gra - - ci - as, De - o gra - - ci - as!
- as, De - o gra - - - - - - ci - as!

* must

4. SUSANNI

A little child there is yborn

Words anon. 15th century

RONALD CORP

Words collated by Percy Dearmer (1867–1936); from the *Oxford Book of Carols* by permission of Oxford University Press

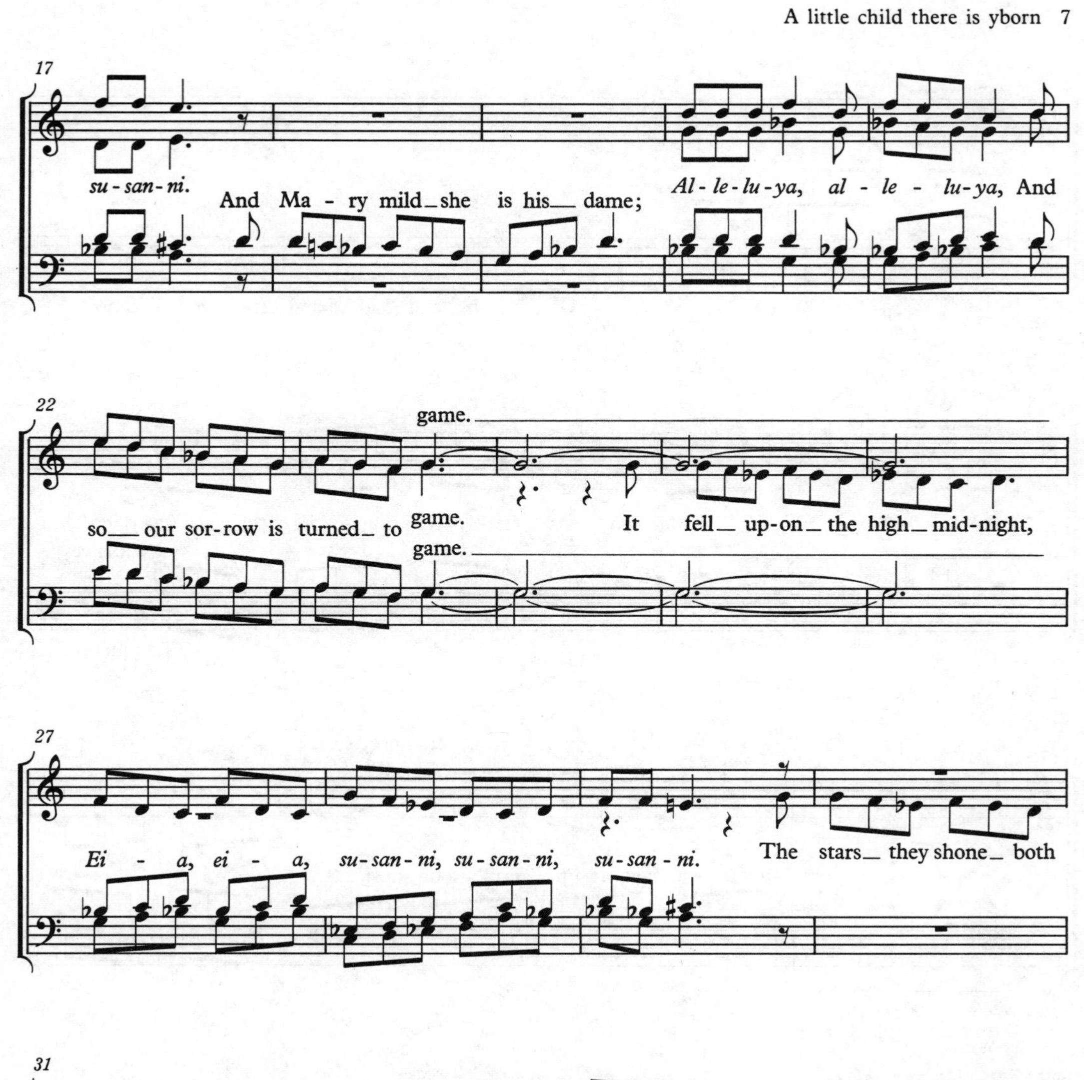
17
su-san-ni.
And Ma - ry mild_she is his_ dame;
Al - le - lu - ya, al - le - lu - ya, And
22
game.
so_ our sor-row is turned_ to
game.
It fell_ up-on_ the high_ mid-night,
game.
27
Ei - a, ei - a, su-san-ni, su-san-ni, su-san-ni.
The stars_ they shone_ both

31
fair_ and bright,
Al - le - lu - ya, al - le - lu - ya
The an - gels sang_ with

35
all_ their might.
Ei - a, ei - a,
might.
Three kings_there came_with their_ pres-ents

40
su - san - ni, su - san - ni, su - san - ni.
Of myrrh and gold and frank-in - cense,
44
Al - le - lu - ya, al - le - lu - ya As clerk - es sing in their se - quence.
se - quence.
se - quence.
48
Now sit we down up - on our knee,
f
Now sit we down up - on our knee,
Ei - a, ei - a,
f
52
su - san - ni, su - san - ni, su - san - ni. And pray we to the Tri - ni - ty,
56
molto rall.
Al - le - lu - ya, al - le - lu - ya, Our help, our suc - cour for to be.

5. THE LITTLE ROAD TO BETHLEHEM

As I walked down the road

Words by
MARGARET ROSE

MICHAEL HEAD

9
dim.
- long the lit - tle road to Beth - le - hem.
dim.
- long the road to Beth - le - hem.
dim.
(mm) A - long the road to
dim.
(Melody)
(mm) A - long the road to

11
p
Be - side the door, as I drew nigh, I
mp
Be - side an o - pen door, as I drew nigh, I
p
Beth - le - hem. I heard sweet
- hem.
p
p
Beth - le - hem. I heard sweet

14
heard a lul - la - by.
heard sweet Ma - ry sing a lul - la - by.
Ma - ry sing a lul - la - by. She
Ma - ry sing.

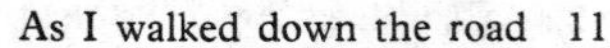

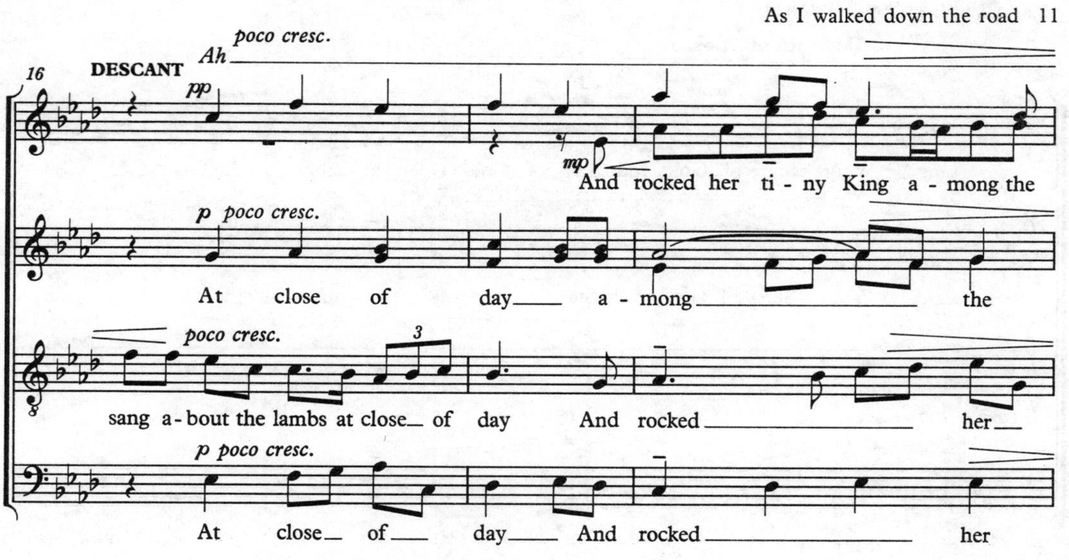
16
DESCANT
poco cresc.
Ah
pp
mp
And rocked her ti - ny King a - mong the
p poco cresc.
At close of day a - mong the
poco cresc.
3
sang a - bout the lambs at close of day And rocked her
p poco cresc.
At close of day And rocked her

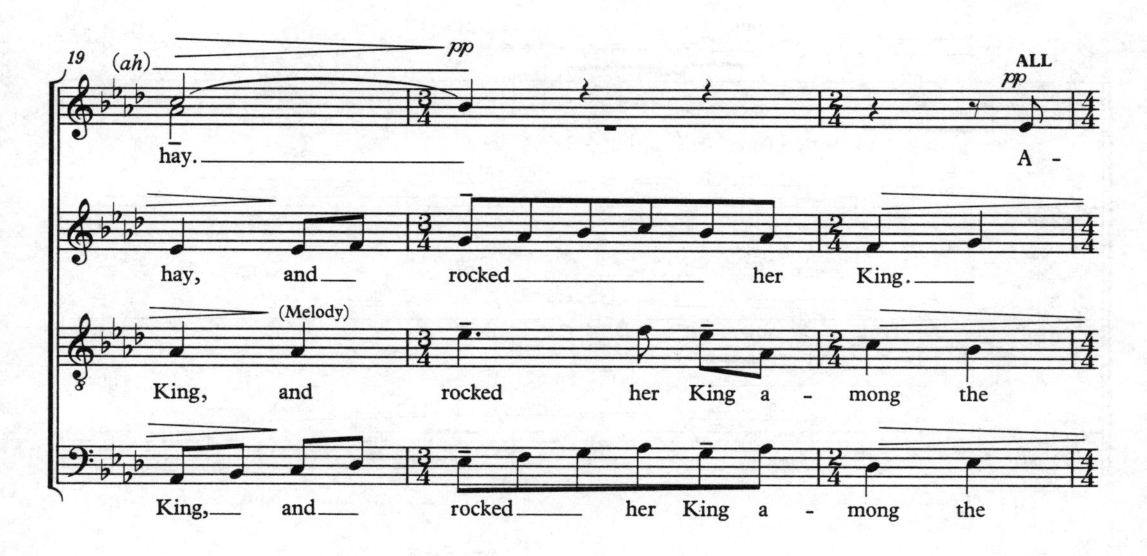
19
(ah)
pp
hay.
ALL
pp
A -
hay, and rocked her King.
(Melody)
King, and rocked her King a - mong the
King, and rocked her King a - mong the

22
poco rit.
- cross the air the sil - ver sheep - bell rang, 'The lambs are com - ing home,' sweet Ma - ry
pp
Mm
pp
hay. Mm
pp
hay. Mm

Poco meno mosso
25
sang, 'Your Star of Gold, your Star of Gold is shi-ning in the sky, So
(mm) 'Your Star of Gold, your Star is shi-ning in the sky, So
(mm) 'Your Star is in the sky, So
(mm) 'Your Star of Gold is shi - - - ning, So
poco rit.
Tempo I
28
sleep, my lit-tle King, go lul-la-by.'
(Melody)
p
sleep, lit-tle King, sleep, my King, go
p
sleep, lul-la-by, go
p
sleep, sleep, my King, go
DESCANT (ad lib.)
Lul - la - by.
30
pp
pp
As I walked down the road at set of sun, The
pp
lul - la-by.' Mm
pp
lul - la-by.' Mm
pp
lul - la-by.' Mm

33
lambs were com - ing home - wards, one by one, I
(mm) I
(mm)
(mm)
35
Ah dim.
poco cresc. pp
heard a sheep-bell soft - ly call - ing them A - long the lit - tle road to Beth - le -
poco cresc. dim.
heard a sheep-bell call - ing them A - long the road to Beth - le -
(✓) poco cresc. dim. (Melody)
(mm) Mm A -
poco cresc. (✓) dim.
(mm) A -
38
(ah) pp e rit. ppp
- hem, the lit - tle road to Beth - le - hem.
e rit. pp ppp
- hem, the lit - tle road to Beth - le - hem.
e pp rit. ppp
- long the road to Beth - le - hem, the road to Beth - le - hem.
e pp rit. ppp
- long the road to Beth - le - hem, the road to Beth - le - hem.

6. FUM, FUM, FUM

Ancient prophets first foretold him

Words anon.

Traditional Spanish carol
arranged by WILLIAM LLEWELLYN

24
fum,
Fum, fum, fum, fum. Come and have your sins for-giv-en: Fum, fum, fum. Come
Fum, fum, fum, fum. Come and have your sins for-giv-en: Fum, fum, fum, fum,
30
join the march-ing throng of Christ-ians, Come, and a-way to fill the church-es With your
fum, fum, fum, fum, fum. Come, and a-way to fill the church-es With your
35
voi-ces prais-ing Hea-ven: Fum, fum, fum, fum, fum, fum, fum, fum,
voi-ces prais-ing Hea-ven: Fum, fum, fum, fum, fum, fum, fum, fum, fum, fum,
41
fp
ff
fum, fum, fum, fum. Fum, fum!
fp
ff
fum, fum, fum, fum, fum, fum, fum, fum, fum!
fp
ff

7. AWAY IN A MANGER

Words anon.

Tune by W. J. KIRKPATRICK
arranged by WILLIAM LLEWELLYN

33
3. Be near me, Lord Jesus, I ask thee to stay Close by me for ever, and
39
SOPRANO SOLO
mp
Bless all the dear children in thy tender care, And
ALL
love me, I pray. Mm, mm,
45
fit us for heaven, to live with thee there.
mm, mm, mm, mm, mm.
pp
mm, mm, mm, mm, mm.

8. DAWN CAROL

Blessed be he that cometh

Gradual and Alleluia in the second
Mass of Christmas, The Mass of Dawn

MALCOLM WILLIAMSON

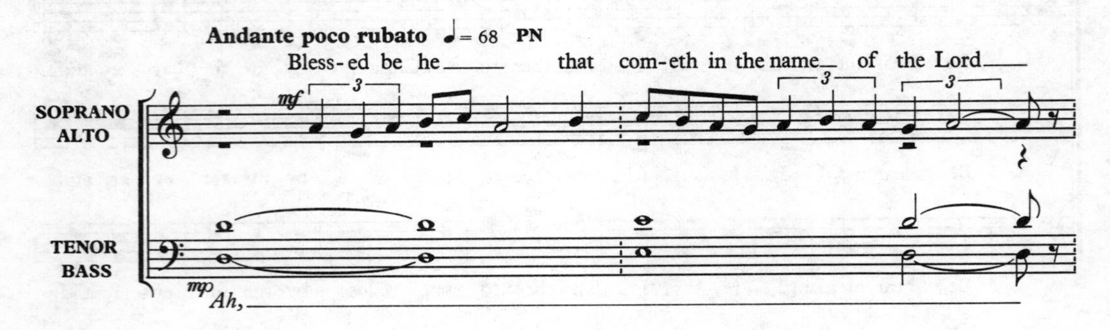

Reprinted by permission of Chappell Music Ltd. and International Music Publications

13
- ia,
cresc.
1 2
- lu - ia, al - le - lu - ia, al - le - lu - ia, al - le - - -
cresc.

2nd time on to Tempo primo
last time
19a
pp
mf
f
- lu - ia, al - le - lu - ia.
- lu - ia, al - le - - - lu - ia,
pp
mf
f

Tempo primo ♩ =68
20b
pp
Fine
Ah,
mp
f
al - le - lu - ia.
The Lord hath reign'd He is
f
mp
Ah,
pp

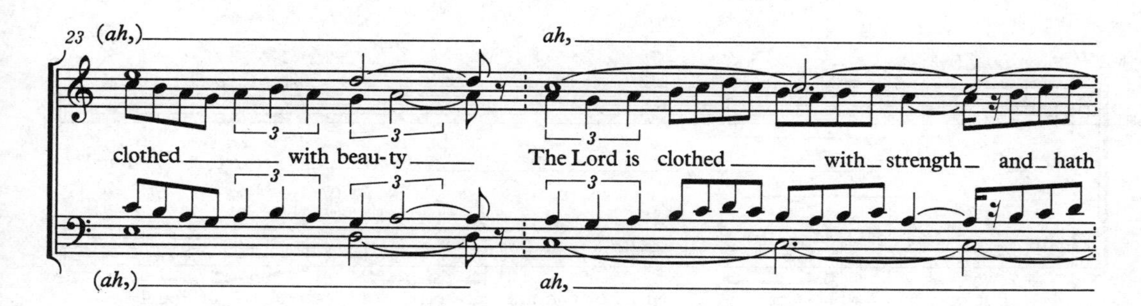
23 (ah,)
ah,
clothed with beau - ty
The Lord is clothed with strength and hath
(ah,)
ah,

D. C. Refrain
without repeat
♩ = 56
25 (ah,)
gird - - - ed Him - self with power.
(ah,)

9. CHRISTMAS IS COMING

Words traditional

WALFORD DAVIES
using traditional melody
for final stanza

This carol is published separately by the Royal School of Church Music.

17
faster
old man's hat. If you have-n't got a pen-ny, a ha' - p'ny 'll do, If you
20
have-n't got a ha' - p'ny, a far - thing 'll do, If you have-n't got a far - thing,
24
Slowly
Quickly
God bless you! God bless the mas-ter of this house, like-wise the mis-tress
30
too, And all the lit - tle chil - dren that round the ta - ble grow. Love and
Love
35
joy come to you and to you your was-sail too, And we wish you, we wish you a
41
hap - py New Year, and we wish you a hap - py New Year. Love and Year.

10. AS JOSEPH WAS A-WALKING

Traditional tune from Rimbault: *Old English Carols* (1865)
arranged by ROBIN WELLS

Words traditional

for Cecily Smithwick and the East Coker W.I.

11. THE OXEN

Words by
THOMAS HARDY

Christmas Eve

BENJAMIN BRITTEN

13
-cur to one of us there To doubt they were kneel-ing then.
3
3
dim.
16
cresc.
So fair a fan-cy few would weave In these years!
p
cresc.
20
Yet, I feel, If some-one said on Christ-mas Eve,
div.
23
moving forward
mf
f
'Come; see the ox-en kneel, see the ox-en kneel In the
mf sustained and cresc.
f heavily

27
lively
S.
lone - ly bar - ton by yon - der coomb Our child-hood used to
A.
lone - ly bar - ton by yon - der coomb Our
31
rall.
dim.
know, our child-hood used to know, See the ox - en
child-hood used to know, used to know, See the ox - en
dim. poco a poco
34
a tempo
unis.
kneel,' I should go with him in the gloom,
expressive
38
Hop-ing it might be so.
molto rit.
dim.
cresc.
expressive

12. A SOMERSET CAROL

Come all you worthy people here

Words traditional
(slightly adapted)

English traditional melody
arranged by WILLIAM LLEWELLYN

*The organ accompaniment may be hummed by the other voices; use the small notes in bars 31–5, ending at the words 'did say.'

42
f ALL
3. God bless his ser - vants in this place That lov - ing - ly do meet; And
f
47
ma - ny hap - py Christ - mas - es To stran - gers in the street. God
ff
51
bless our ge - ne - ra - tion, Who live both far and near, And we wish them a
cresc.
56
S.
A.
hap - py, a hap - py New Year, a hap - py New Year!
T.
B.
New Year, New Year!
ff

13. DING-DONG, DING

Words by
G. R. WOODWARD

Melody *O quam mundum, quam jucundum* from *Piae Cantiones*
harmonized by G. R. WOODWARD

14. DE VIRGIN MARY HAD A BABY BOY

Words traditional

West Indian spiritual
arranged by WILLIAM LLEWELLYN

*The orchestral accompaniment provides a 2-bar introduction.

Melody and words from *The Edric Connor Collection of West Indian Spirituals and Folk Tunes* by permission of Boosey and Hawkes Music Publishers Ltd.

14
glo - ry,
He come_ from the glo - rious king - dom,
come from the glo - ry, he come from the glo - ry, the glo - rious king - dom, he
17
He come_ from the glo - ry,
He come_ from the glo - rious king-dom.
come from the glo - ry, he come from the glo - ry, he come from the glo - ry, the glo - rious king-dom.
21
f
O, yes, be - lie - ver, O, yes, be - lie - ver,
pp
He come_ from the glo - ry,
Org.
Ped.
p
Man.
27
pp
mf cresc.
f cresc.
He come_ from the glo - rious king-dom. Dum, dum, dum,_dum, dum, dum, dum, dum, dum,_dum, dum, dum,

31
SOLO (any voice)
3. De Wise Men saw when de
ff
ppp
dum, dum, dum, dum, dum, dum, dum, dum, dum, dum, dum, dum, dum, dum, dum,
34
ba-by born, De Wise Men saw where de ba-by born, De
dum, dum, dum, dum, dum, dum, dum, dum, dum, dum, dum, dum, dum, dum, dum,
dum,
37
Wise Men went where de ba-by born, And dey say dat his name was Je-sus.
dum, dum, dum, dum, dum, dum, dum, dum, dum, dum, dum, his name was Je-sus.
41
SOLO mf
CHORUS mf
SOLO f
O, yes, be-lie-ver, O, yes, be-lie-ver, O, yes, be-lie-ver!
Org. mp
Man.

47
CHORUS pp
rit.
Slow with a swing
ff SOLO
O, yes, be-lie-ver!
He come from the glo-ry,
pp
Ped.
f
51
fff ALL
He come from the glorious king-dom,
He come from the glo-ry,
ff
55
SOLO
a tempo
He come from the glo-rious
pppp
Dum, dum, dum, dum, dum, dum,
59
in tempo al fine
ppp
king-du-mm.
p
dum, dum, dum, dum, dum, dum, dum, dum, dum, dum, dum, dum, dum,
king-du-mm.

15. DING DONG! MERRILY ON HIGH (i)

Words by
G. R. WOODWARD

French 16th century tune
arranged by WILLIAM LLEWELLYN

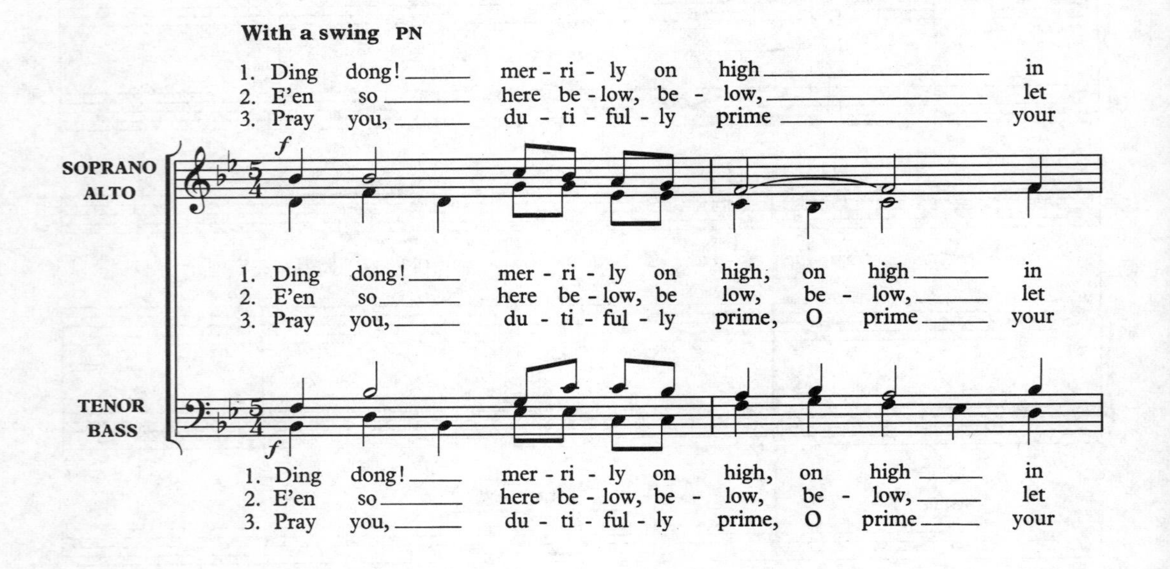

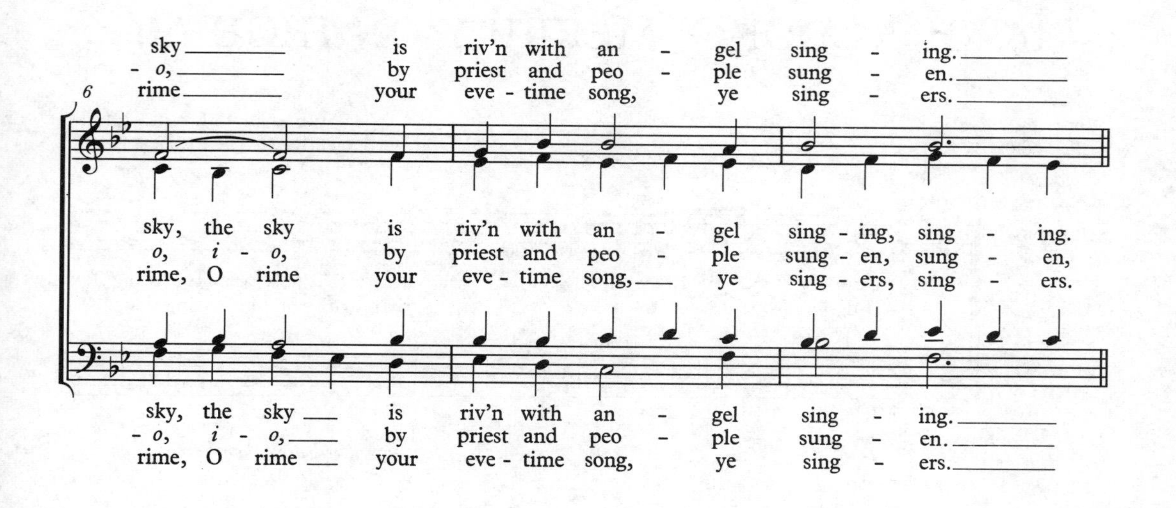
sky is riv'n with an - gel sing - ing.
- o, by priest and peo - ple sung - en.
6 rime your eve - time song, ye sing - ers.
sky, the sky is riv'n with an - gel sing - ing, sing - ing.
o, i - o, by priest and peo - ple sung - en, sung - en,
rime, O rime your eve - time song, ye sing - ers, sing - ers.
sky, the sky is riv'n with an - gel sing - ing.
- o, i - o, by priest and peo - ple sung - en.
rime, O rime your eve - time song, ye sing - ers.

Glo
9
Glo - ri - a, sing, Glo - ri - a, sing, Glo - ri - a, sing,

12 ri - a, Ho -
Ho -
Glo - ri - a, sing, Glo - ri - a, Ho -

15 - san - na in ex - cel - sis! - cel - sis!
1
2
- san - na
- san - na in ex - cel - sis, sing, - cel - sis!

16. DING DONG! MERRILY ON HIGH (ii)

Words by
G.R. WOODWARD

French 16th century tune
arranged by H. LE FEVRE POPE

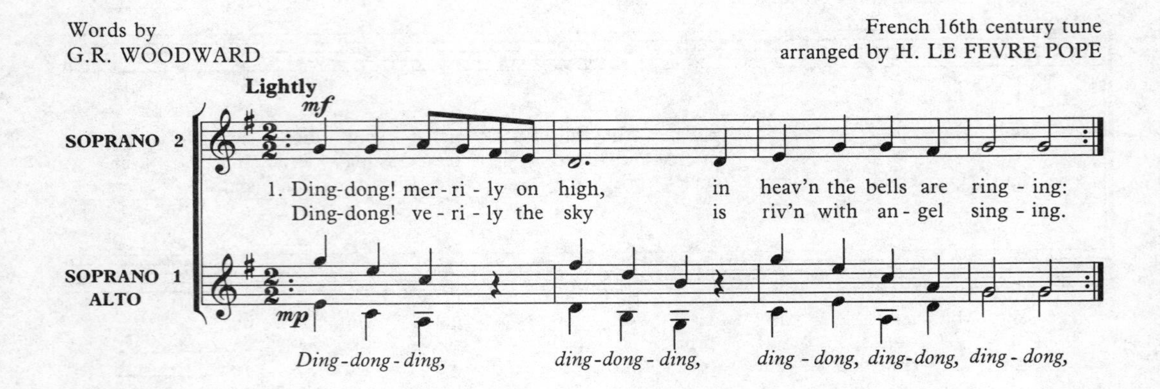

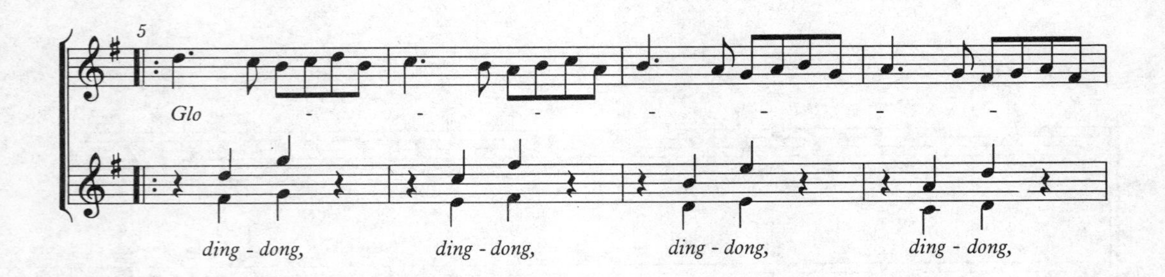

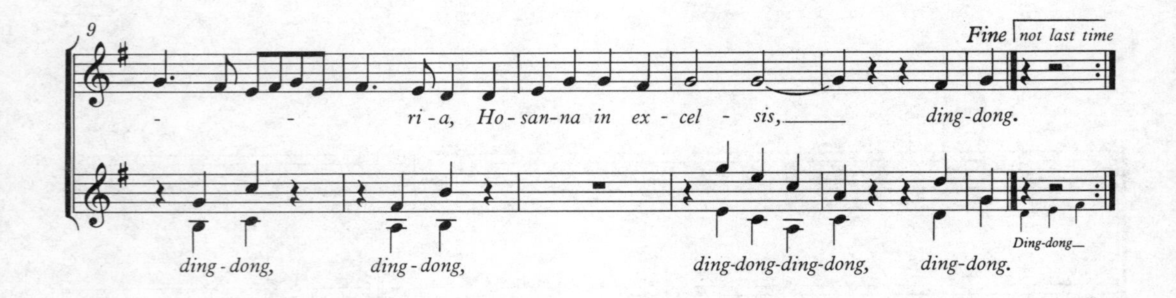

2. E'en so here below, below,
let steeple bells be swungen,
And *io, io, io,*
by priest and people sungen,

3. Pray you, dutifully prime
your mattin chime, ye ringers;
May you beautifully rime
your evetime song, ye singers.

17. DONKEY PLOD AND MARY RIDE

Words by
TIMOTHY DUDLEY-SMITH

ERIC H. THIMAN
arranged by WILLIAM LLEWELLYN

Melody by Eric Thiman from *The Path to the Moon* by permission of Boosey and Hawkes Music Publishers Ltd.

poco ten.
mf
a tempo
T.
mf
mp
2. Ma-ry's child, on Christ-mas Eve, none_ but ox_ and ass re-ceive; theirs the man-ger
B.
mp
mf
mp
mf
mp
mp
mp
and_ the stall where_ is laid the Lord_ of all—
down the years re-mem-ber them,
mp
mf
mp
mp
(mp)
(mp)
come_ a-way,_
Piano
come_ a-way,_ come a-way, come_ a-way_ to Beth-le-hem.
come a-way,
Piano
S.
f
A.
3. An-gels throng the mid-night sky: 'Glo-ry be_ to
f

42
God on high'. Theirs the song that sounds_ a-broad, 'Born_ a Sa-viour.
46
mp
Christ_ the Lord'—
down the years re-mem-ber them,
mp
p
51
p
cresc.
come_ a-way,_ come_ a-way,_ come_ a-way_ to Beth-le-hem.
f
cresc.
f
mf
55
poco ten.
dim.

a tempo
S.
A.
T.
B.
4. Shep - herds haste the watch to keep where their Ma - ker lies a - sleep;
theirs the an - gels' pro - mised sign, 'Born for us a child di - vine'—
down the years re - mem - ber them, come a - way, come a - way,
come a - way,
come a - way to Beth - le - hem.
Piano
5. An - cient kings from east - ern skies trace the way of all the wise,
theirs the shi - ning star, to find light to light - en all man-kind— down the years re -

84
come a-way,
mp
-mem - ber them, come a-way, come a - way, come a-way to Beth - le-hem.
mf
come a-way,
(mp)
89
cantabile
poco ten.
mf
93
a tempo
S. mf
A.
6. Shep-herds, kings and an - gel throngs, teach us where our joy be-longs:
T.
B. mf
a tempo
97
f
souls re-stored and sins for-given, Christ on earth the hope of heaven —
f

101
f
down the years re - joice — in them,
f
mp
p
105
mf
come — a - way, —
cresc.
f
come — a - way, — come a - way, — come — a - way — to Beth - le -
mf
cresc.
f
cresc.
f
109
poco rall.
p
pp
- hem.
p
pp
poco rall.
p
mf
pp
Ped.

18. OUR LADY'S LULLABY (i)

Dormi Jesu

Words anon. 18th century

PHILIP RILEY

19. OUR LADY'S LULLABY (ii)

Dormi Jesu

Words anon. 18th century

RICHARD RODNEY BENNETT

Allegretto ♪=126 **PN**

SOPRANO 1
SOPRANO 2
ALTO

p

Dor - mi Je - su, Ma - ter ri - det
Dor - mi Je - su, Ma - ter ri - det
Dor - mi Je - su, Ma - ter ri - det

5

Quae tam dul - cem som - num vi - det, Dor -
Quae tam dul - cem som - num vi - det, Dor -
Quae tam dul - cem som - num vi - det, Dor - mi

10

mf pp mp

- mi Je - su blan - du - le. Si non
- - mi Je - su blan - du - le. Si non
Je - su blan - du - le. Si non

14

poco cresc.

dor - mis, Ma - ter plor - at, In - ter fi - la
dor - mis, Ma - ter plor - at, In - ter fi - la
dor - mis, Ma - ter plor - at, In - ter fi - la

Two Lullabies No. 1

19
mf
can - tans or - at. Blan - - de ve - nit
can - tans or - at. Blan - - - - de ve - nit
can - tans or - at. Blan - de ve - nit
23
p
pp
som - nu - le. Dor - mi Je - su, Ma - ter
som - nu - le. Dor - mi Je - su, Ma - ter
som - nu - le. Dor - mi Je - su, Ma - ter
28
più f
dim.
ri - det Quae tam dul - cem som - num vi - det,
ri - det Quae tam dul - cem som - num vi - det,
ri - det Quae tam dul - cem som - num vi - det,
33
Poco più lento
Dor - mi Je - su, blan - du - le.
Dor - - - mi Je - su, blan - du - le.
Dor - mi, Dor - mi Je - su, blan - du - le.

20. HARK! THE HERALD ANGELS SING

Words by
C. WESLEY, T. WHITEFIELD
M. MADAN, and others

From a chorus in MENDELSSOHN'S *Festgesang* (1840)
originally adapted by W. H. CUMMINGS
Introduction and arrangement
of last verse by WILLIAM LLEWELLYN

21
With the an - gel - ic host pro - claim, Christ is born in Beth - le - hem.
Pleased as man with man to dwell, Je - sus, our Em-man - u - el.
HARMONY
25
UNISON
Hark! the her - ald an - gels sing Glo - ry to the new-born King.
Org.
DESCANT
29
3. Hail the heav'n-born Prince of peace! Hail the Sun of Right-eous -
UNISON VOICES
3. Hail the heav'n - born Prince of peace! Hail the Sun of Right-eous -
Org.
32
- ness! Light and life to all he brings, Ris'n with heal - ing in his
- ness! Light and life to all he brings, Ris'n with heal - ing in his

36
as a fanfare
wings; Hark! the her - ald an - gels
wings; Mild he lays his glo - ry by, Born that man no more may
40
sing, Hark! the her - ald an - gels sing, Hark! the her - ald an - gels
die, Born to raise the sons of earth, Born to give them sec - ond
44
sing. Hark! the her - ald an - gels sing Glo - ry to the new-born King.
birth. Hark! the her - ald an - gels sing Glo - ry to the new-born King.

21. A FANFARE FOR CHRISTMAS

Vespers for Christmas Day

Hodie, hodie

ROBIN WELLS

This Fanfare may be used as an introduction immediately preceding a hymn.

*Bars A and B are alternatives for use as appropriate to the succeeding key.

22. GOD REST YOU MERRY, GENTLEMEN

21
ti - dings of com - fort and joy.
f
26
S.
A.
mf
2. From God our heaven-ly Fa - ther A bless-ed an-gel
T.
B.
mf
30
came, And un-to cer-tain shep - herds Brought ti - dings of the
34
same, How that in Beth-le - hem was born The Son of God by name:
f ALL
39
O ti - dings of com - fort and joy, comfort and joy: O
f
Ped.

43
ti - dings of com - fort and joy.
f
mf
mp
48
T.
p
3. But when to Beth - le - hem they came, Where - at this in - fant
B.
p
p
52
lay, They found him in a man - ger, Where ox - en feed on
56
hay; His moth - er Ma - ry kneel - ing, Un - to the Lord did pray:
f ALL
61
O ti - dings of com - fort and joy, comfort and joy: O
f
Ped.

65
ti - dings of com - fort and joy.
70
S.
A.
4. Now to the Lord sing prais - es, All you with - in this
T.
B.
74
place, And with true love and bro - ther - hood Each oth - er now em -
78
-brace; This ho - ly tide of Christ - mas All oth - ers doth de - face:
Ped.

ALL
83
O ___ ti - dings of com - fort and joy, comfort and joy: O ___
87
ti - dings of com - fort and joy.
f
92
f
5. God bless the rul - er of this house, And long on may he
simile
96
reign, And ma - ny hap - py Christ - mas - es He live to see a -

100
-gain. God bless our ge - ne - ra - tion, That live both far and near, And God

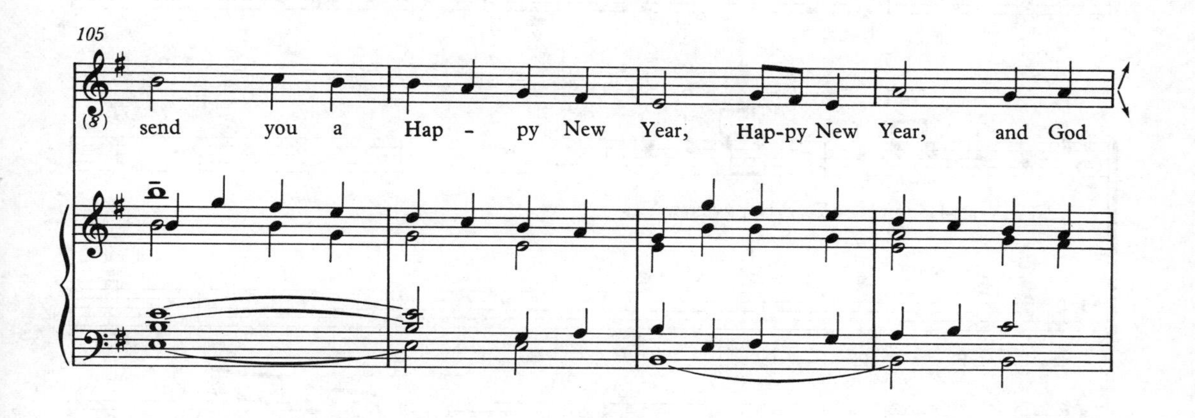
105
send you a Hap - py New Year, Hap-py New Year, and God

109
S.
send you a Hap - py New Year.
A.
send you a Hap - py New Year.
send you a Hap - py New Year.
T.
B.
send you a Hap - py New Year.
f

114
dim.
pp
cresc. molto
Happy New Year! Happy New Year! Happy
Hap - py New Year!
dim.
pp cresc. molto
mf
mp
ppp
119
f
New Year! Happy New Year! Happy New Year!
ff
Hap-
Hap - py New Year!
f
ff
f
124
- py New Year!
ff
sf
Man.
Ped.

23. HOW SOFT, UPON THE EV'NING AIR

Words by
IRENE GASS

THOMAS F. DUNHILL
arranged by WILLIAM LLEWELLYN

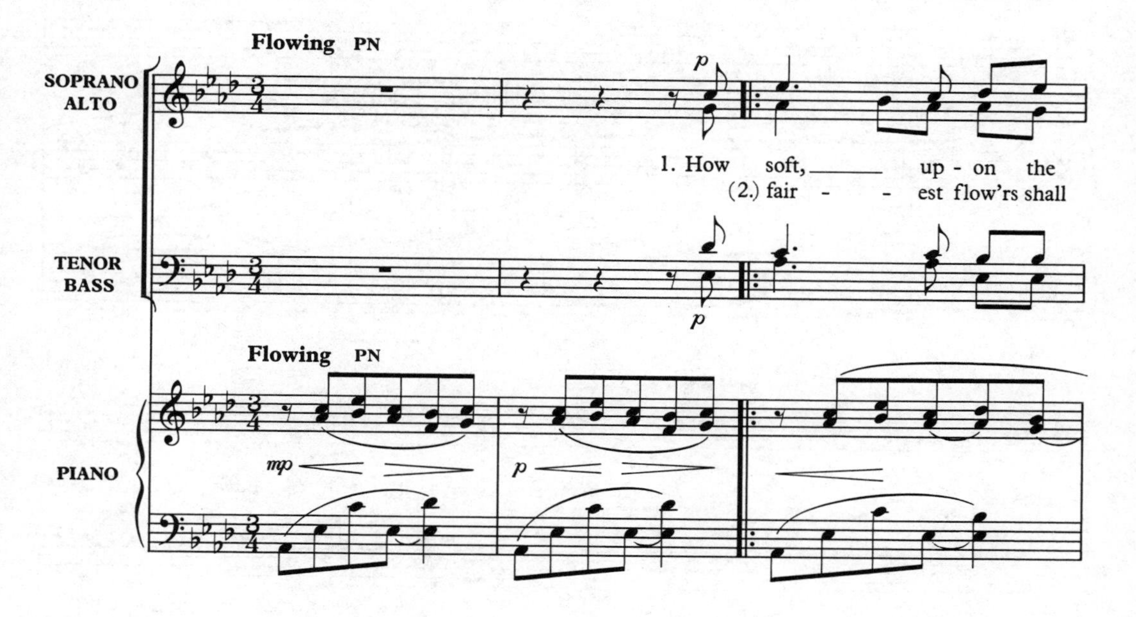

sooth-ing mu-sic of the pipes, From
run-ning streams and sing-ing birds shall
The sooth-ing mu-sic From shep-herds on the
While sing-ing birds Shall bring to Him sweet
mf
mu-sic From
and birds Shall
poco rit.
a tempo
pp
hill.
praise.
See how He sleeps, my love-ly Babe, With-
-in His man-ger bed, While si-lent-ly the
While
ppp

16
1
poco rit.
a tempo
moon glides by And stars keep watch o'er - head.
pp
19a
2
2. The stars keep watch o'er -
mp
p
18b
- head.
Mm.
calando
pp
ppp

for Philip Colls

24. SLUMBER SONG OF THE MADONNA

Hushaby low

Words by
ALFRED NOYES

RONALD FINCH

31
sing?
p
sing, to sing?
know what to sing? Here in my arms as I swing thee to
sing, to sing?
sing?
p
SOLO fp
Hush - - - a - by low, Rock - -
37
sleep. Mm, mm, mm,
p
sim.
44
- - a - by so.
dim.
Ah, ah
Mm, mm,
50 a tempo
meno mosso
pp sub.
ALL Kings may have won - der - ful Mo-ther has on - ly a
mf
Kings may have je - wels to bring. Mo-ther has Mo - ther has on - ly a
mf
pp sub.
Mo - ther has
56
kiss for her King.
sfp
Ah - a Ah
sfp
on - ly a kiss.
ah.
Ah - a - ah, ah - a -
kiss for her King.
SOLO
ALL
on - ly a kiss.
sfp

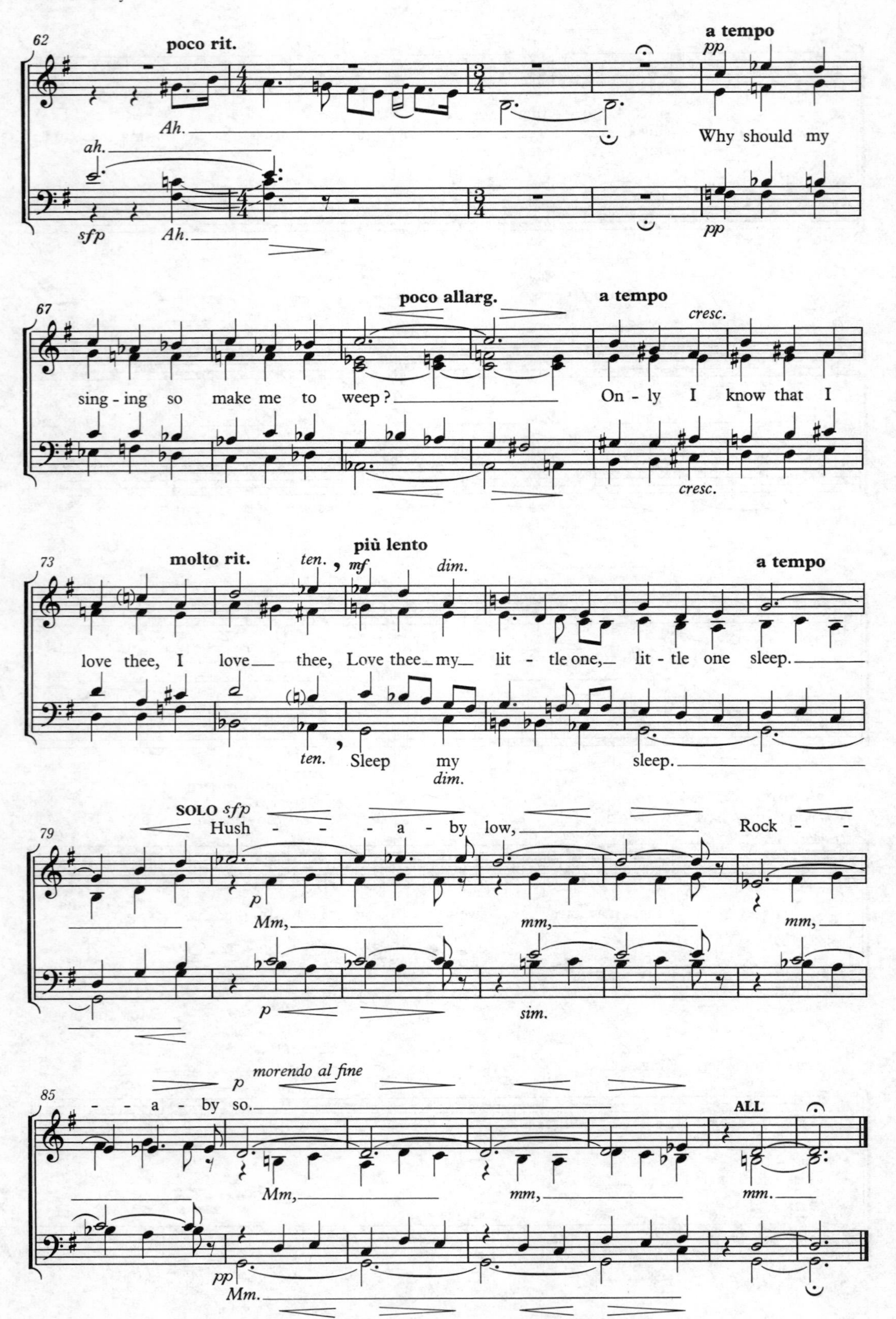
62
poco rit.
a tempo
pp
Ah.
Why should my
ah.
sfp
Ah.
pp
67
poco allarg.
a tempo
cresc.
sing - ing so make me to weep?
On - ly I know that I
cresc.
73
molto rit.
ten.
più lento
mf
dim.
a tempo
love thee, I love thee, Love thee my lit - tle one, lit - tle one sleep.
ten.
Sleep my sleep.
dim.
SOLO sfp
Hush - - a - by low,
Rock - -
79
p
Mm,
mm,
mm,
p
sim.
85
p
morendo al fine
- - a - by so.
ALL
Mm,
mm,
mm.
pp
Mm.

25. HUSH YOU, MY BABY

Words by
TIMOTHY DUDLEY-SMITH

WILLIAM LLEWELLYN

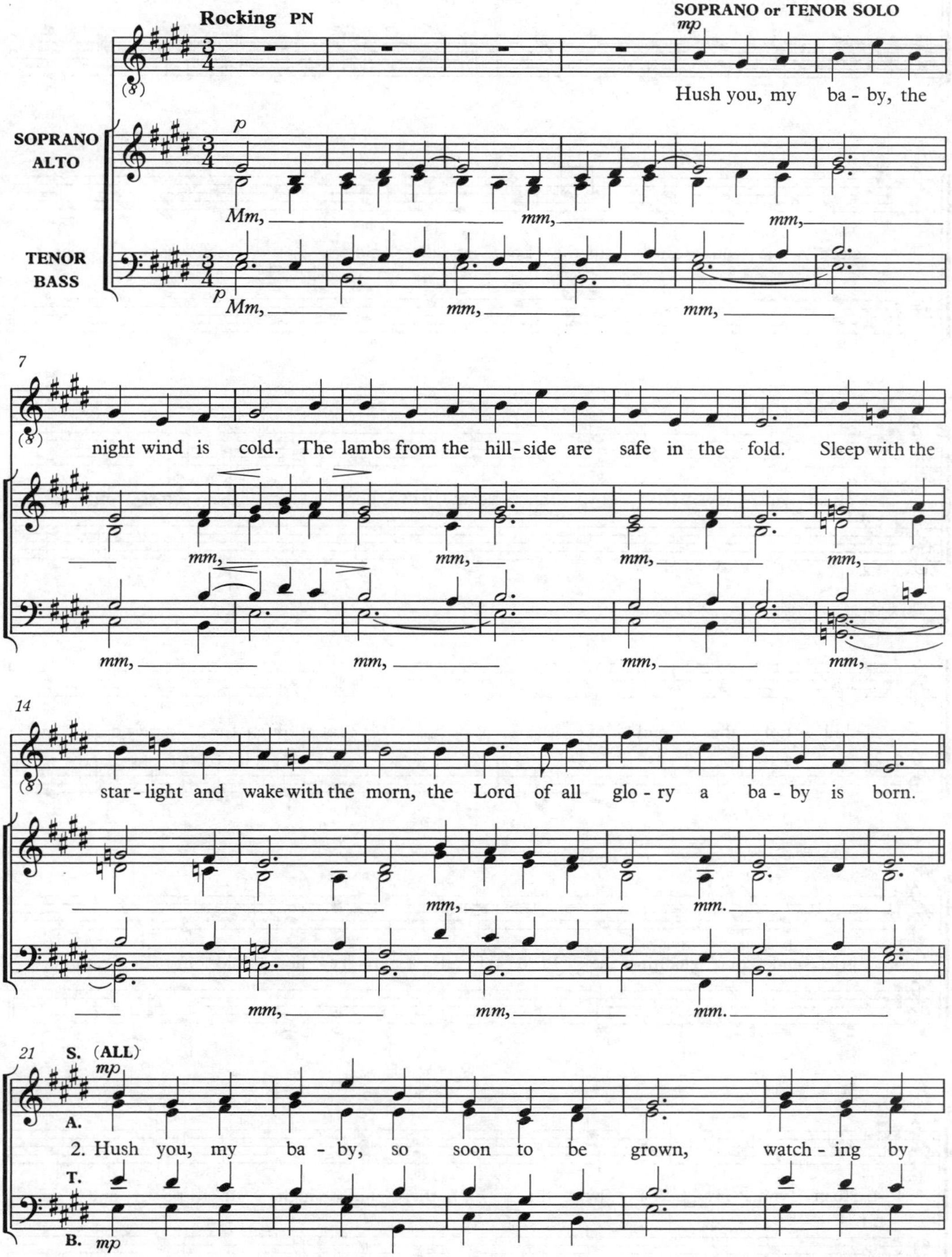

Rocking PN

SOPRANO or TENOR SOLO

mp

Hush you, my ba - by, the night wind is cold. The lambs from the hill-side are safe in the fold. Sleep with the star-light and wake with the morn, the Lord of all glo - ry a ba - by is born.

SOPRANO ALTO

p Mm, mm, mm, mm, mm, mm, mm, mm, mm.

TENOR BASS

p Mm, mm, mm, mm, mm, mm, mm, mm, mm, mm.

S. (ALL) *mp*

A.

2. Hush you, my ba - by, so soon to be grown, watch - ing by

T.

B. *mp*

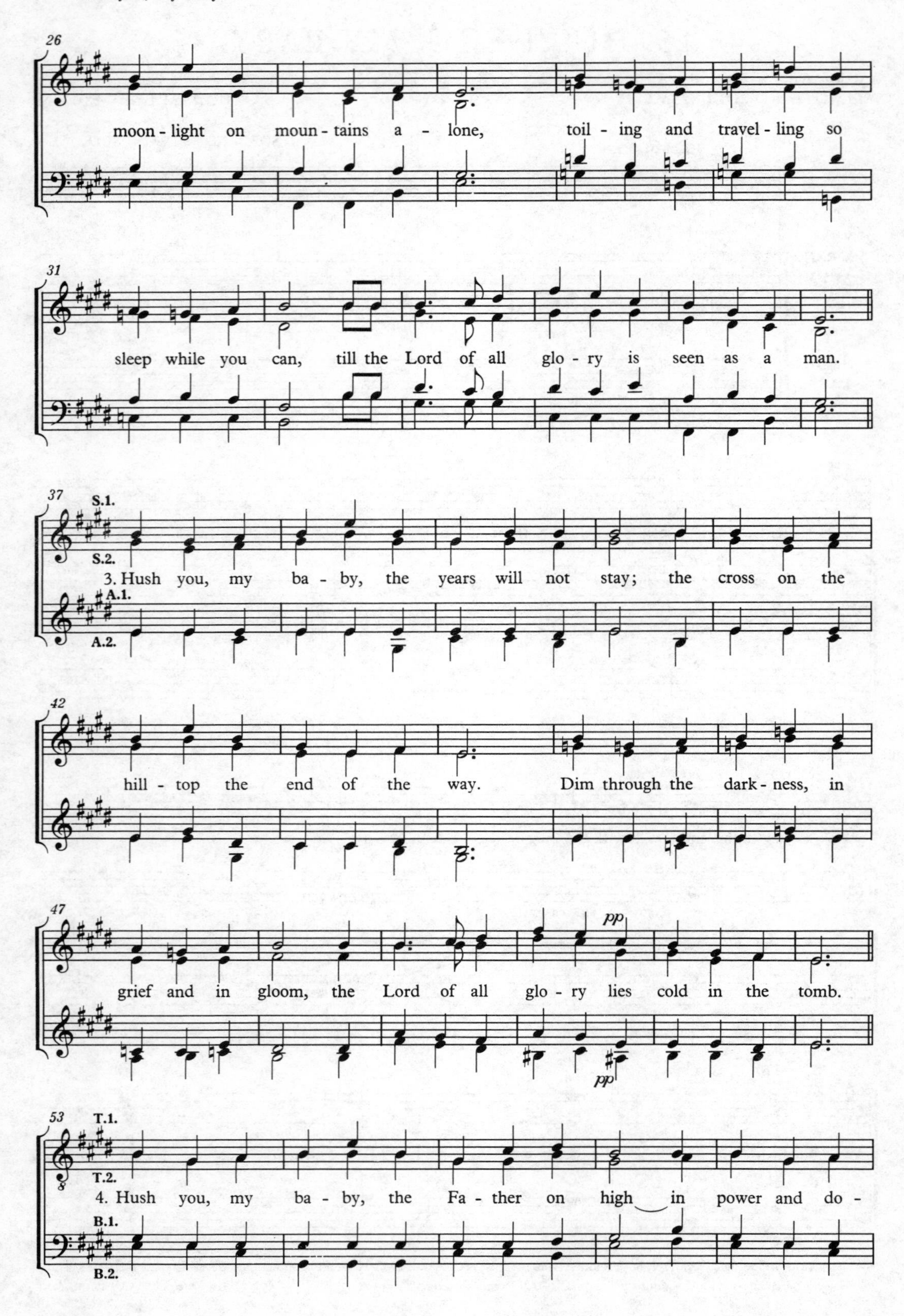
26
moon - light on moun - tains a - lone, toil - ing and travel - ling so
31
sleep while you can, till the Lord of all glo - ry is seen as a man.
37
S.1.
S.2.
3. Hush you, my ba - by, the years will not stay; the cross on the
A.1.
A.2.
42
hill - top the end of the way. Dim through the dark - ness, in
47
grief and in gloom, the Lord of all glo - ry lies cold in the tomb.
pp
pp
53
T.1.
T.2.
4. Hush you, my ba - by, the Fa - ther on high in power and do -
B.1.
B.2.

58
-min - ion the dark - ness puts by. Bright from the shad - ows, the
63
seal and the stone, the Lord of all glo - ry re - turns to his own.
69
SOLO VOICES (S. and T.)
S.
5. Hush you, my ba - by, the sky turns to
A.
Mm, mm, mm, mm,
T.
B.
Mm, mm, mm,
76
gold; the lambs on the hill - side are loose from the fold. Fast fades the
crescendo
Ah, ah,
mm, mm.
Ah,
Fast fades the
mm, mm.
Ah,
crescendo
82
mid-night and new springs the morn, for the Lord of all glo - ry a Sa-viour is born.
ff
ah, ah,
ah, ah,
mid-night and new springs the morn, for the Lord of all glo - ry a Sa-viour is born.
ah, ah, ah, ff

26. TROC-A-TRON

I'm a-ridin' to Bethlehem

English words by
JAMES WOODHOUSE

Czech tune arranged
by PETR EBEN

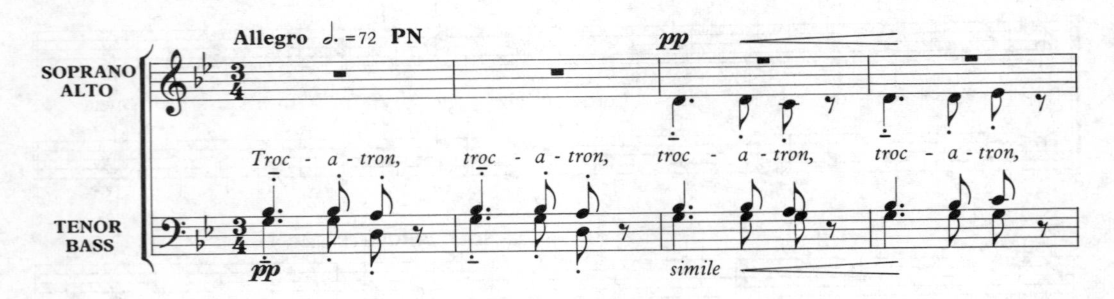

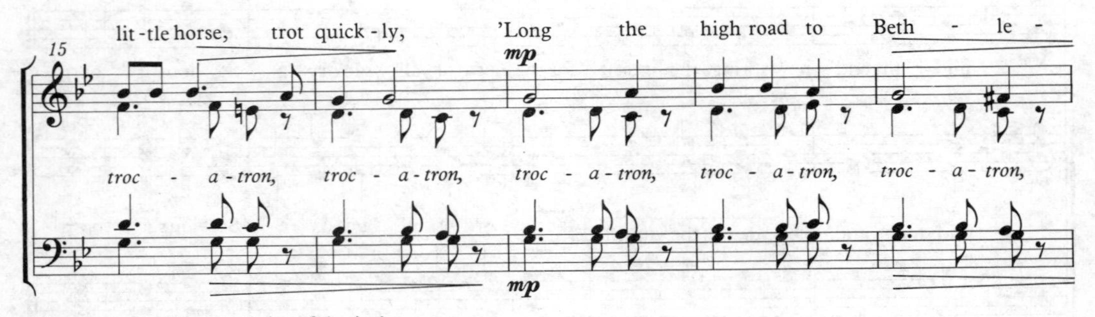

- hem.
20
troc - a - tron, troc - a - tron, troc - a - tron, troc - a - tron, troc - a - tron,
pp
troc,
25
mp simile
troc - a - tron, troc - a - tron, troc - a - tron, troc - a - tron, troc - a - tron,
mf marc.
'Long the high road to Beth - le - hem, Rid - in' to
30
poco f
troc - a - tron, troc - a - tron, troc - a - tron, troc - a - tron, troc - a - tron,
f marc.
decresc.
see him in Beth - le - hem. Lit-tle horse, trot quick-ly,
35
p dolce
troc - a - tron, troc - a - tron, ah, yah, troc - a - tron,
p dolce
lit-tle horse, trot quick-ly, Soon I'll see him in Beth - le -
40
pp troc.
pp troc.
troc - a - tron, troc - a - tron, troc - a - tron, troc - a - tron, troc - a - tron, troc.
- hem.
ppp

27. IN DULCI JUBILO

Words translated from
the German source of 1570
by R. L. PEARSALL

Old German melody
set by R. L. PEARSALL
arranged for four voices
by W. J. WESTBROOK

17
SOLI
le - ni -
3. O Pa - tris ca - ri - tas! O Na - ti le - ni -
Pa - tris ca - ri - tas! O Na - ti le - ni - tas!
21
- tas!
Deep were we stain-ed Per no - stra cri - mi -
- tas! Deep - ly were we stain - ed Per no - stra cri - mi -
Deep - ly were we stain - ed Per no - stra cri - mi - na; But
25
- na;
But Thou hast for us gain-ed
- na; But Thou, Thou hast gain - ed Cœ - lo - rum gau - di -
Thou hast for us gain - ed Cœ - lo - rum gau - di - a:
29
mf O that
ALL
- a: O that we, that we were there, O that we were there!
ALL
mf
ALL
mf O that we,
S.
33
f
4. U - bi sunt gau - di - a, where, If that they be not there?
A. f
4. U - bi sunt gau - di - a, If that they be not there?
T.
f
4. U - bi sunt gau - di - a, where, If that they be not there?
B.
f
4. U - bi, u - bi sunt gau - di - a, where, If not there?

37
p SOLI
There, are an - gels sing - ing No - va can - ti - ca; There,
p SOLI
There, are an - gels sing - ing, There, there, the bells,
p SOLI
There, are an - gels sing - ing, there, are sing - ing can - - ti -
p SOLI
There, are an - gels sing - - ing, The

41
the bells are ring - - ing In Re - gis cu - ri -
there, the bells are ring - ing In Re - gis cu - ri - a:
- ca; The bells are ring - ing In cu - ri -
bells are ring - ing there In Re - gis cu - ri -

45
f ALL
- a: O that we were there, O that we were there!
f ALL
O that we were there, that we were there! There,
f ALL
- a: O that we were there, O that we were there!
f ALL
- a: O that we were there! There, are an - gels

49
There, are an - - gels sing - ing, There, the bells are ring - -
are an - gels sing - ing, There the bells are ring - -
There, are an - gels sing - ing, There, the bells are ring - ing, the
sing - ing, There, the bells, are ring - ing, the bells are ring - -

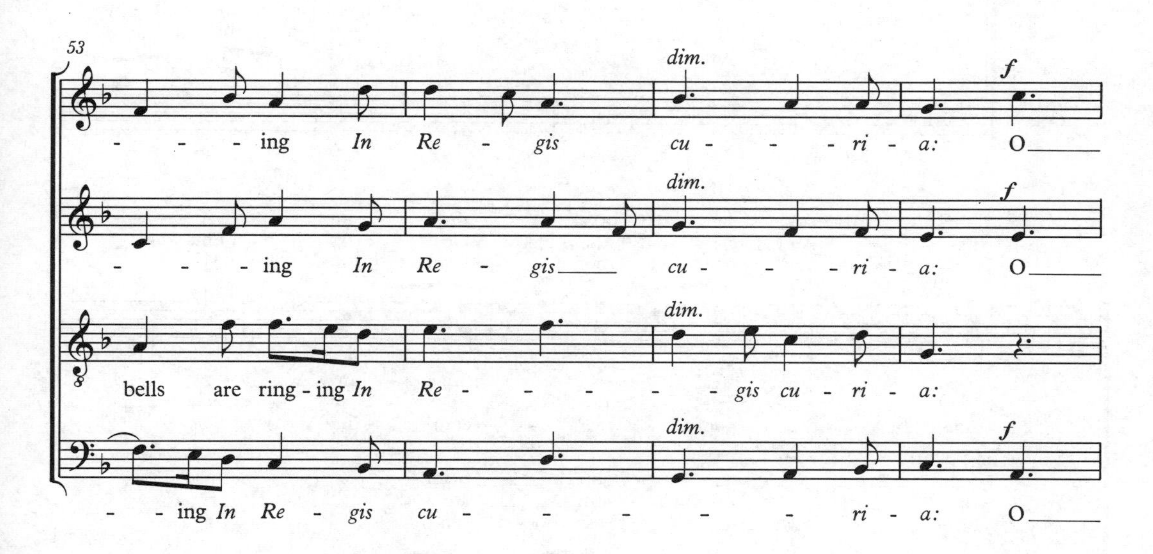
53
dim.
f
- - - ing In Re - gis cu - - - ri - a: O
- - - ing In Re - gis cu - - - ri - a: O
bells are ring - ing In Re - - - - - gis cu - ri - a:
- - ing In Re - gis cu - - - - - ri - a: O

57
dim.
f
that we were there, O that we were there!
that we were there, O that we were there!
O that we were there, O that we were there!
that we were there, O that we were there!

for the Capilla Classica Polifonica of Barcelona

28a. THE SONG OF THE BIRDS

In this most joyful night

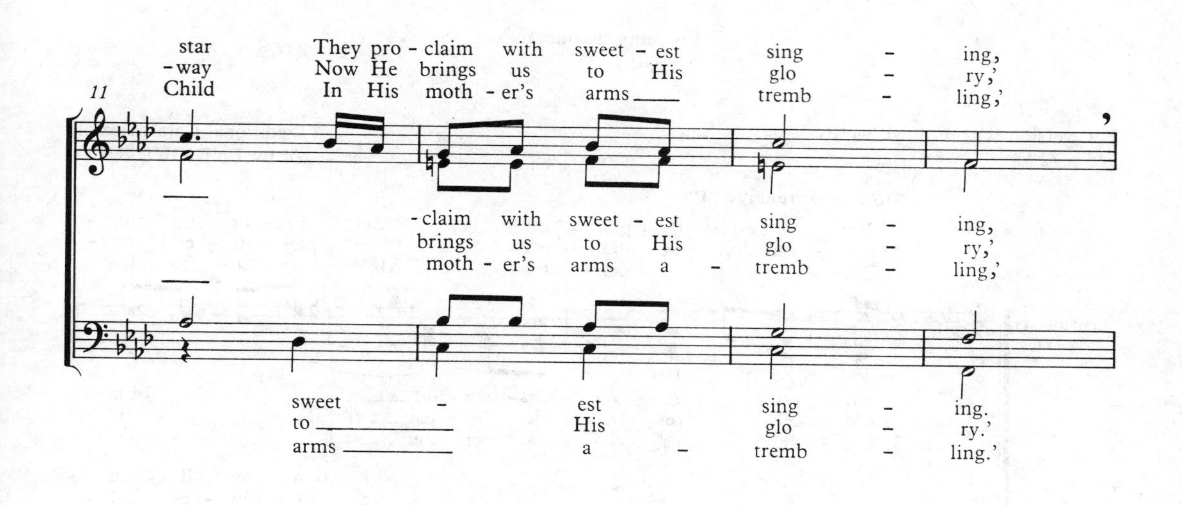
11
star They pro - claim with sweet - est sing - ing,
-way Now He brings us to His glo - ry,'
Child In His moth - er's arms tremb - ling,'
-claim with sweet - est sing - ing,
brings us to His glo - ry,'
moth - er's arms a - tremb - ling,'
sweet - est sing - ing.
to His glo - ry.'
arms a - tremb - ling.'

15
A light more dazz - ling far Than an - y sun or
'This Je - sus, born to - day, Our sin hath swept a -
'My nest in here I'll build, So I can see the
Ah,
Ah,

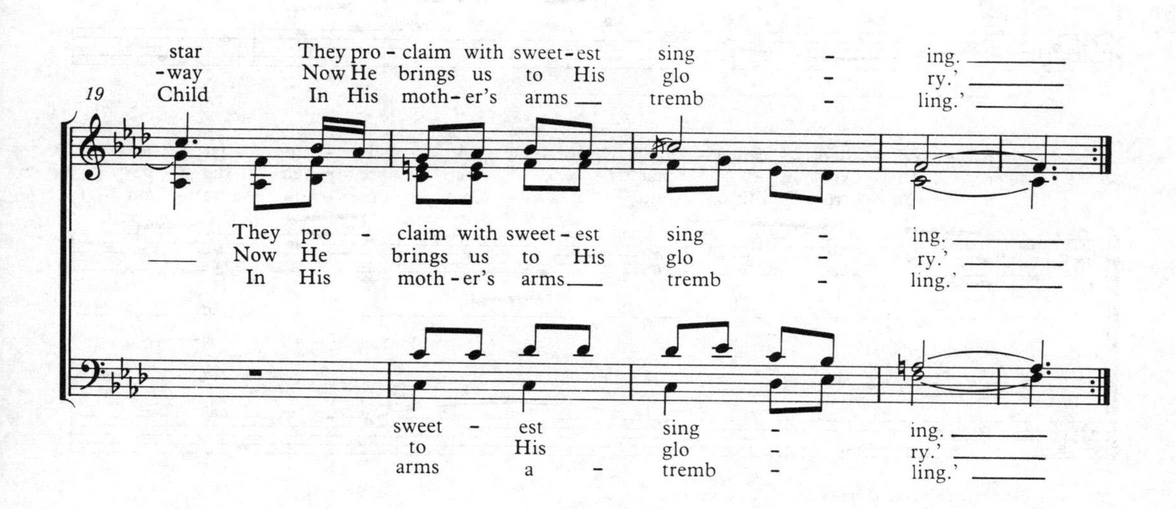
19
star They pro - claim with sweet - est sing - ing.
-way Now He brings us to His glo - ry.'
Child In His moth - er's arms tremb - ling.'
They pro - claim with sweet - est sing - ing.
Now He brings us to His glo - ry.'
In His moth - er's arms tremb - ling.'
sweet - est sing - ing.
to His glo - ry.'
arms a - tremb - ling.'

for the Capilla Classica Polifonica of Barcelona

28b. EL CANT DES OCELLS

En veure despuntar

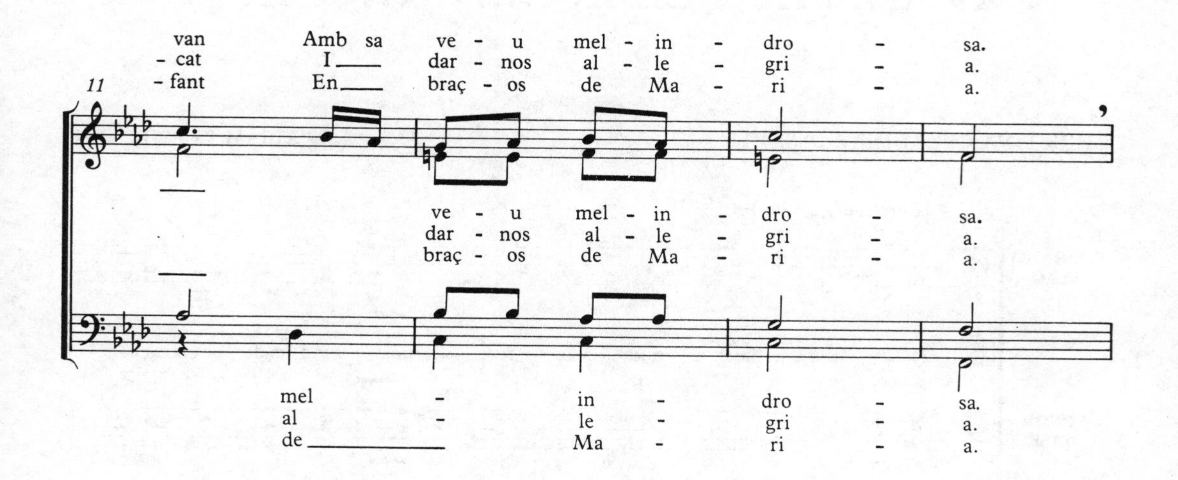
van Amb sa ve - u mel - in - dro - sa.
- cat I dar - nos al - le - gri - a.
11 - fant En braç - os de Ma - ri - a.
ve - u mel - in - dro - sa.
dar - nos al - le - gri - a.
braç - os de Ma - ri - a.
mel - in - dro - sa.
al - le - gri - a.
de Ma - ri - a.

Els o - ce - llets can - tant A fes - te - jar - lo
Di - ent Je - sus es nat Per treu - re'ns del pe -
15 Per a veu - re l'In - fant com es - ta tre - mo -
Ah,

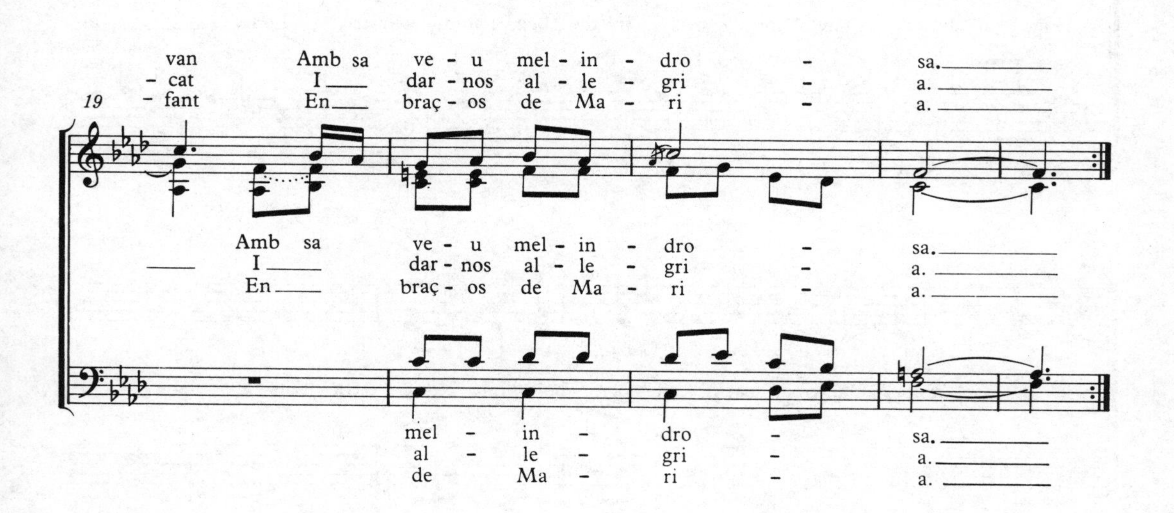
van Amb sa ve - u mel - in - dro - sa.
- cat I dar - nos al - le - gri - a.
19 - fant En braç - os de Ma - ri - a.
Amb sa ve - u mel - in - dro - sa.
I dar - nos al - le - gri - a.
En braç - os de Ma - ri - a.
mel - in - dro - sa.
al - le - gri - a.
de Ma - ri - a.

for Mildred

29. IN THE BLEAK MID-WINTER (i)

mp
Heav'n and earth shall flee a - way When he comes to reign. In the
mp
bleak mid - win - ter A sta - ble-place suf - ficed The Lord God Al -
migh - y, Je - - sus Christ. 3. E - nough for him, whom
Che - ru - bim Worship night and day, A breastful of milk, And a
man-ger - ful of hay; E - nough for him, whom an - gels Fall down be -

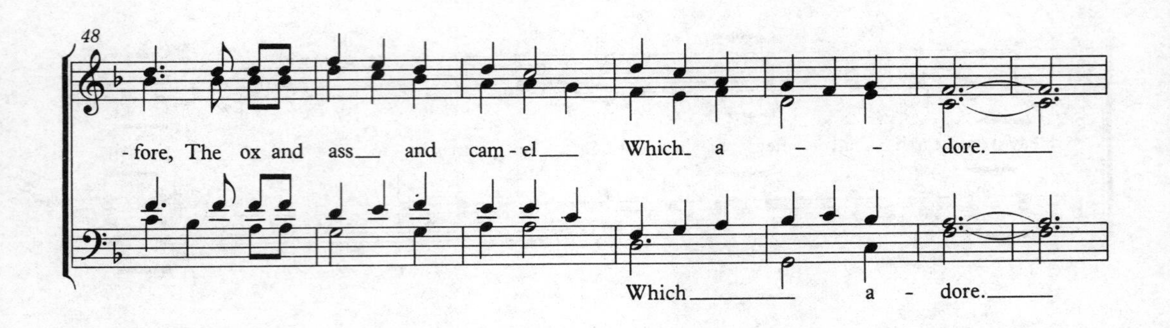
48
-fore, The ox and ass and cam-el Which a - - dore.
Which a - dore.

Firmly
55
f
cresc.
4. An-gels and arch-an-gels May have ga-thered there, Che - ru-bim and se - ra-phim
f
cresc.

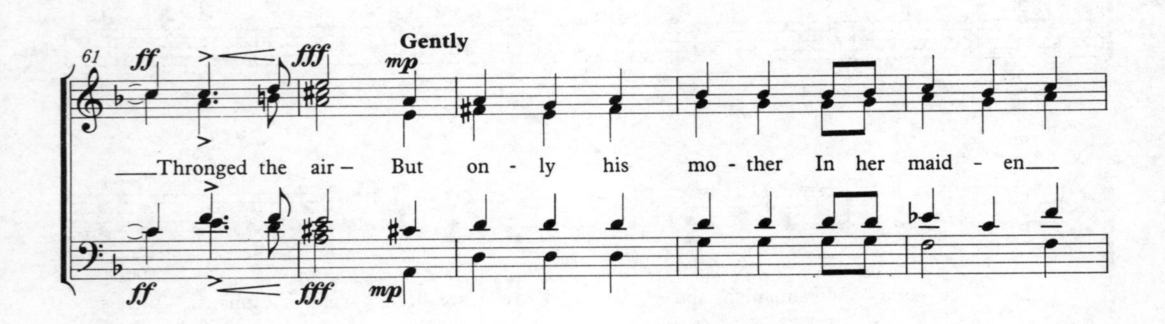
61
ff
fff
Gently
mp
Thronged the air – But on - ly his mo-ther In her maid - en
ff
fff
mp

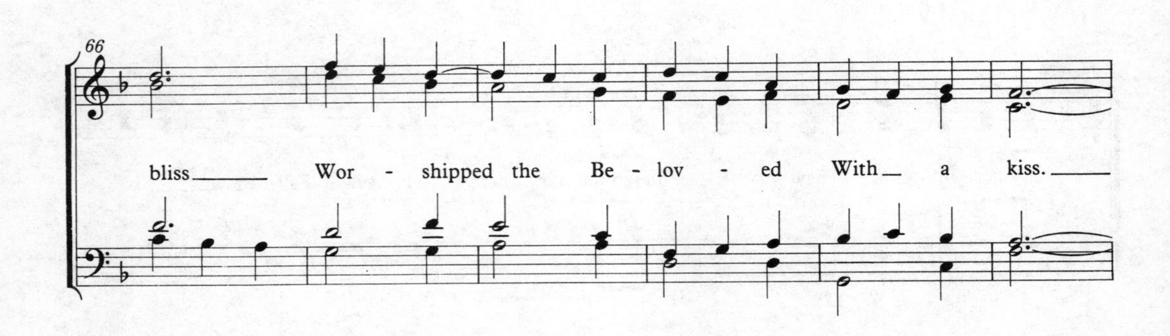
66
bliss Wor - shipped the Be - lov - ed With a kiss.

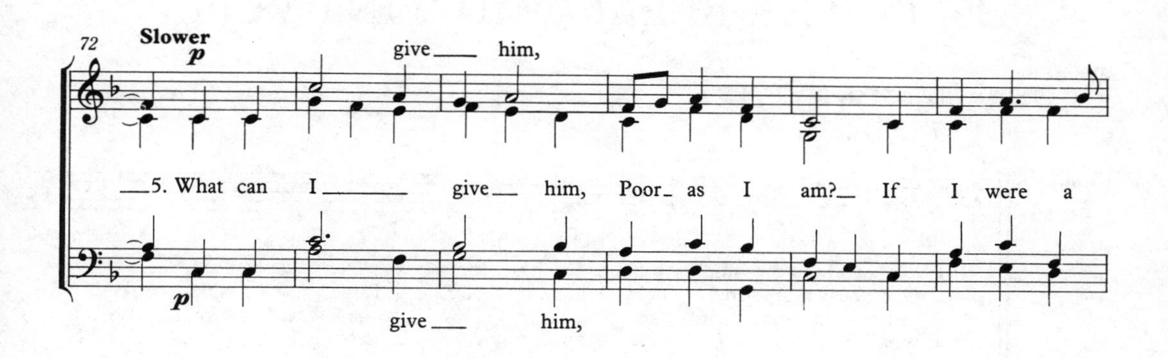
72
Slower
p
give___ him,
___5. What can I ______ give___ him, Poor_ as I am?__ If I were a
p
give___ him,

78
shep-herd I would bring__ a lamb;__ If I were a wise man I would

83
Steadying
f
pp
do my___ part; Yet what I can___ I give him – Give ______
f
pp
Give ______

88
ppp
rit.
p
______ my heart, ______ give ______ my heart. ______
p
ppp
my ______ heart, ______ give ______ my ______ heart. ______

30. IN THE BLEAK MID-WINTER (ii)

Words by
CHRISTINA GEORGINA ROSETTI

GUSTAV HOLST

31. NINNA-NANNA A GESÙ BAMBINO

In thy mother's arms

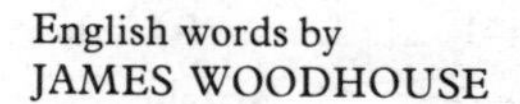

English words by
JAMES WOODHOUSE

D. LAVINIO VIRGILI

13
p
cie - lo. Ve - glia il cie - lo, o Di - o Bam - bi - no, che con
sky. An - gels watch in the sky. Child of Heav'n, sweet - ly lie. By the
pp mm,
mm, mm, mm,
pp

18
l'a - stro ri - lu - cen - te se - gni ai Ma - gi il pi - o cam - mi - no so - pra i
star a - bove thee shin - ing Wise men find the sac - red way, O'er the
mm, mm, mm,
mm, mm,

22
p
mon - ti, so - pra il ma - re: dor - mi e la - scia - ti cul -
hills, o - ver the sea, Gifts of love bring - ing thee. Sleep and let the cra - dle
pp mm, mm,
mm, mm,
pp

27
pp
-la - re, dor-mi e la-scia-ti cul - la - re, dor - mi, dor - mi e
rock you, sleep and let the cra - dle rock you. Sleep and dream, and
mm,
mm,
mm,
mm,
mm,
mm,

32
rall.
più lento
dolcissimo
so - gna.
Dor-mi e so-gna in fra - gil ve - lo sul tuo
dream.
Sleep and dream, with an - gels keep - ing Watch a -
pp
ppp
mm,
mm,
mm,
mm,
mm,
mm,
mm,
mm,
mm,

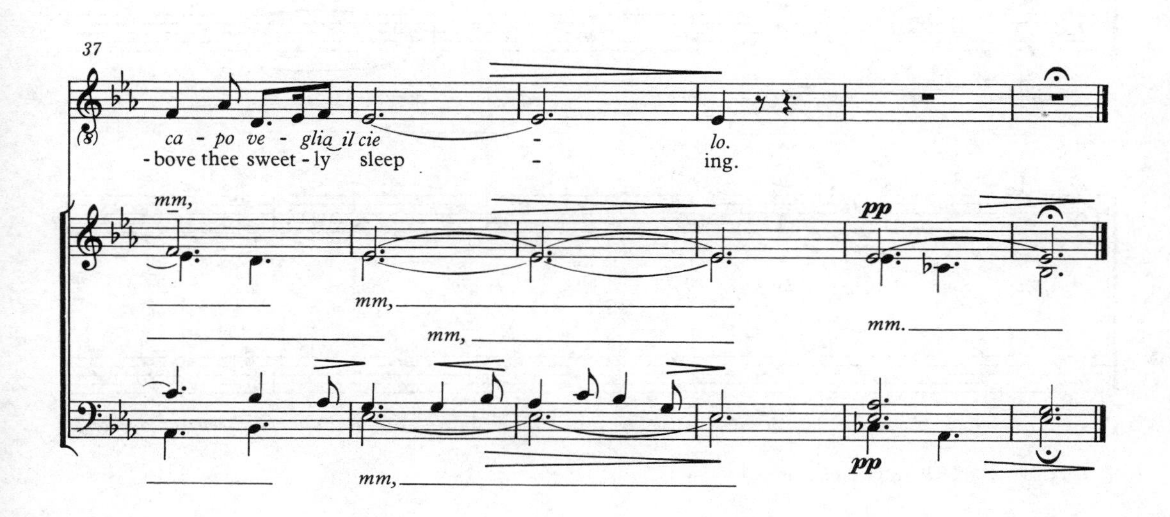
37
ca - po ve - glia il cie - lo.
-bove thee sweet - ly sleep - ing.
mm,
pp
mm,
mm,
mm.
pp
mm,

for the Linden Singers

32. I SAW THREE SHIPS (i)

Words traditional

English carol
arranged by IAN HUMPHRIS

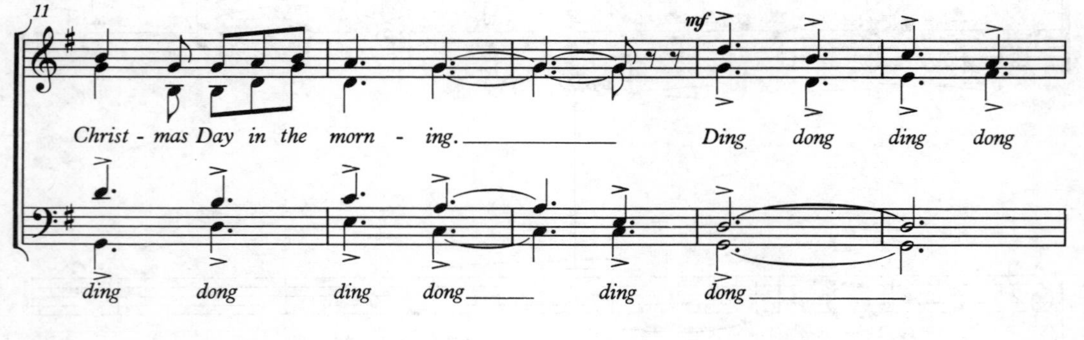

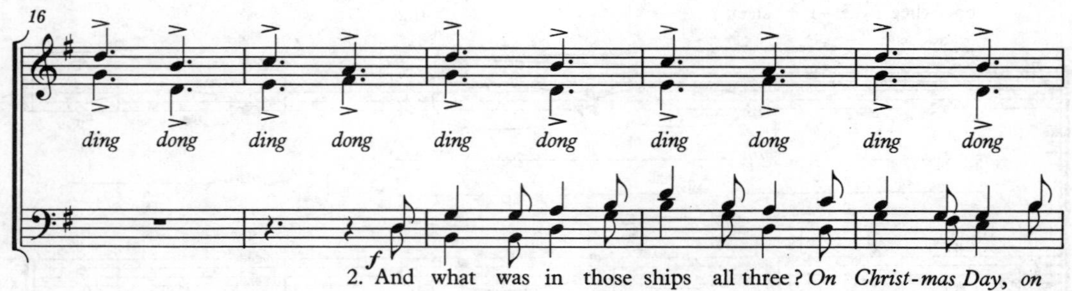

21
dim.
ding dong ding dong ding dong ding dong ding dong
Christ-mas Day, And what was in those ships all three? On Christ-mas Day in the morn - ing.
dim.
26
ding dong
mp
mf
ding.
3. Our
mp
Ding dong ding dong ding dong ding dong
31
Sa - viour Christ and his la - dy, On Christ-mas Day, on Christ-mas Day, Our Sa - viour Christ and
ding dong ding dong ding dong ding dong ding dong
36
dim.
his la - dy, On Christ - mas Day in the morn - ing.
Ding dong
ding dong ding dong ding dong ding dong
dim.
41
ding.
p
ding dong ding dong ding dong dong ding dong ding.
dong
p
ding.

for Charterhouse

33. I SAW THREE SHIPS (ii)

Words traditional

Two English tunes
arranged by WILLIAM LLEWELLYN

Tempo I ♩.=120 PN
TENORS and BASSES (SOLI *ad lib.*)

p

1. I saw three ships come sail - ing in, *On Christ-mas Day, on Christ-mas Day,* I

5

saw three ships come sail - ing in, *On Christ - mas Day in the morn - ing.*

Tempo II ♩.=96

I saw three ships come sail - ing in, *Christ - mas Day, Christ - mas Day,*

S.

mf 9

A.

I saw three ships come sail - ing in, sail - ing, *Christ - mas Day, Christ - mas Day,* I

T. ALL

B. ALL mf

sail - ing, *Christ - mas, Christ - mas,*

On Christ - mas

13

saw three ships come sail - ing in, *On Christ - mas Day in the morn - ing.*

sail - ing in, *On Christ - mas Day*

Tempo I
TENORS and BASSES (SOLI *ad lib.*)

mf 17

2. And what was in those ships all three? *On Christ-mas Day, on Christ-mas Day,* And
4. Pray whi - ther sailed those ships all three? Pray,

21

what was in those ships all three? *On Christ - mas Day in the morn - ing.*
whi - ther sailed those ships all three?

Tempo II
S.
A.
T.
B.
25
3. The Vir - gin Ma - ry and Christ were there, Christ - mas Day, Christ - mas Day, The
5. O, they sailed in - to Beth - le - hem, Christ - mas Day, Christ - mas Day, O,
Christ there, Christ - mas, Christ - mas,
Beth - lem,
29
On Christ - mas
Vir - gin Ma - ry and Christ were there, On Christ - mas Day in the morn - ing.
they sailed in - to Beth - le - hem,
On Christ - mas Day
Tempo I
33
Don! don! don! don!
6. And all the bells on earth shall ring, On Christ - mas Day, on Christ - mas Day, And
37
all the bells on earth shall ring, On Christ - mas Day in the morn - ing.
Tempo II
41
7. And all the an - gels in heav'n shall sing, Christ - mas Day, Christ - mas Day, And
Christ - mas Day, Christ - mas Day,

45
all the an-gels in heav'n shall sing, On Christ - mas Day in the morn - ing, on
On Christ - mas Day, on Christ- mas Day in the

Christ - mas Day in the
49
Fast ♩. =132
ff
Christ - mas, the morn - ing. 8. Then let us all re - joice a-main! On Christ-mas Day, On
morn - ing, on Christ-mas Day.
ff

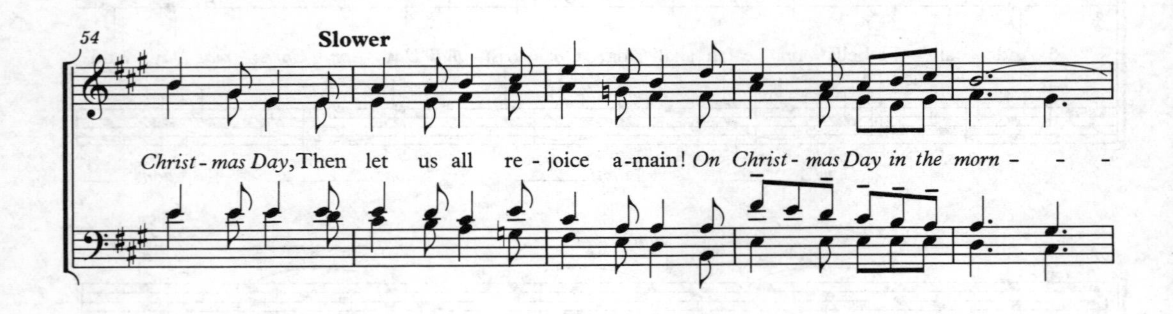
54
Slower
Christ- mas Day, Then let us all re - joice a-main! On Christ - mas Day in the morn - - -

Tempo I
dim.
ppp
59
T. SOLO
p
B. SOLO
I saw three ships come sail - ing in, On Christ- mas Day in the morn - ing.
- - - ing.

34. I SING OF A MAIDEN

Words traditional
15th century

ROBIN WELLS

* chose: pronounce 'chezz'

for the Choir of King's College, Cambridge

35. ILLUMINARE, JERUSALEM

Jerusalem rejos for joy

Words anon. 15th century
Bannatyne MS *f*.27v

JUDITH WEIR

[1] star [2] king

Suddenly mysterious and urgent
16
S.
p subito
mp
p
Il - lu - min - a - re, Je - ru - sa - lem.
A.
p subito
mp
p
Il - lu - min - a - re, Je - ru - sa - lem.
T.
p subito
mp
p
Il - lu - min - a - re, Je - ru - sa - lem.
B.
p subito
mp
p
Il - lu - min - a - re, Je - ru - sa - lem.
Suddenly mysterious and urgent
8′(+16′)
Org.
pp :in the background, soft but weighty
Ped.
16′(+32′)
20
Lightly: with a little more movement
S.
mf
With an-gell-is licht in le - gi - o - nis thou art il - lu - mi - nit
A.
mf
With an-gell-is licht in le - gi - o - nis thou art il - lu - mi - nit
T.
mf
With an-gell-is licht in le - gi - o - nis thou art il - lu - mi - nit
24
mp
p misterioso
all a - bout. Three king-is of strange re - gi - o - nis
mp
p misterioso
all a - bout. Three king-is of strange re - gi - o - nis
mp
p misterioso
all a - bout. Three king-is of strange re - gi - o - nis

[1] at once, all together

[1] held, harboured [2] worthy

51
Broadening
does nem,
a tempo
men his glo - ri - ous name does nem, hea-ven, hea-ven, erd and hell mak - is in - cly - ning:
nem, hea-ven,
men his glo - ri - ous name does nem, hea-ven, erd and hell mak - is in - cly - ning:
men his glo - ri - ous name does nem, hea-ven, hea-ven, erd and hell mak - is in - cly - ning:
men his glo - ri - ous name does nem.

55
Il - lu-min - a-re, Je - ru - - sa - lem.
Il - lu-min - a-re, Je - ru - - sa - lem.
Il - lu-min - a - re, Je - ru - - sa...
Il - lu-min - a-re, - sa - lem.

36. JESUS, JESUS, REST YOUR HEAD

Words traditional

Appalachian carol
arranged by ARTHUR WARRELL

17
mf
How his mo - ther went to that sta - ble On that Christ-mas eve so late?
mf
21
poco rall.
f
Winds were blow - ing, cows were low - ing, Stars were glow-ing, glow - ing, glow-ing.
glow - - - ing.
Winds were blow - - - - ing, Stars were glow-ing.
f
25
a tempo
pp
rest,
Rest,
Rest,
rest,
All the e - vil
mp
pp
Je - sus, Je - sus, rest your head, You have got a man-ger bed; rest,
p
pochiss. rall.
a tempo
30
rest,
rest,
rest,
folk on earth Sleep in feath-ers at their birth; Je - sus, Je - sus, rest your head,
rest,
Je - sus,
35
rest.
rest.
You have got a man-ger bed. To that man-ger came then wise men, Bring-ing things from
mf
rest.
mf

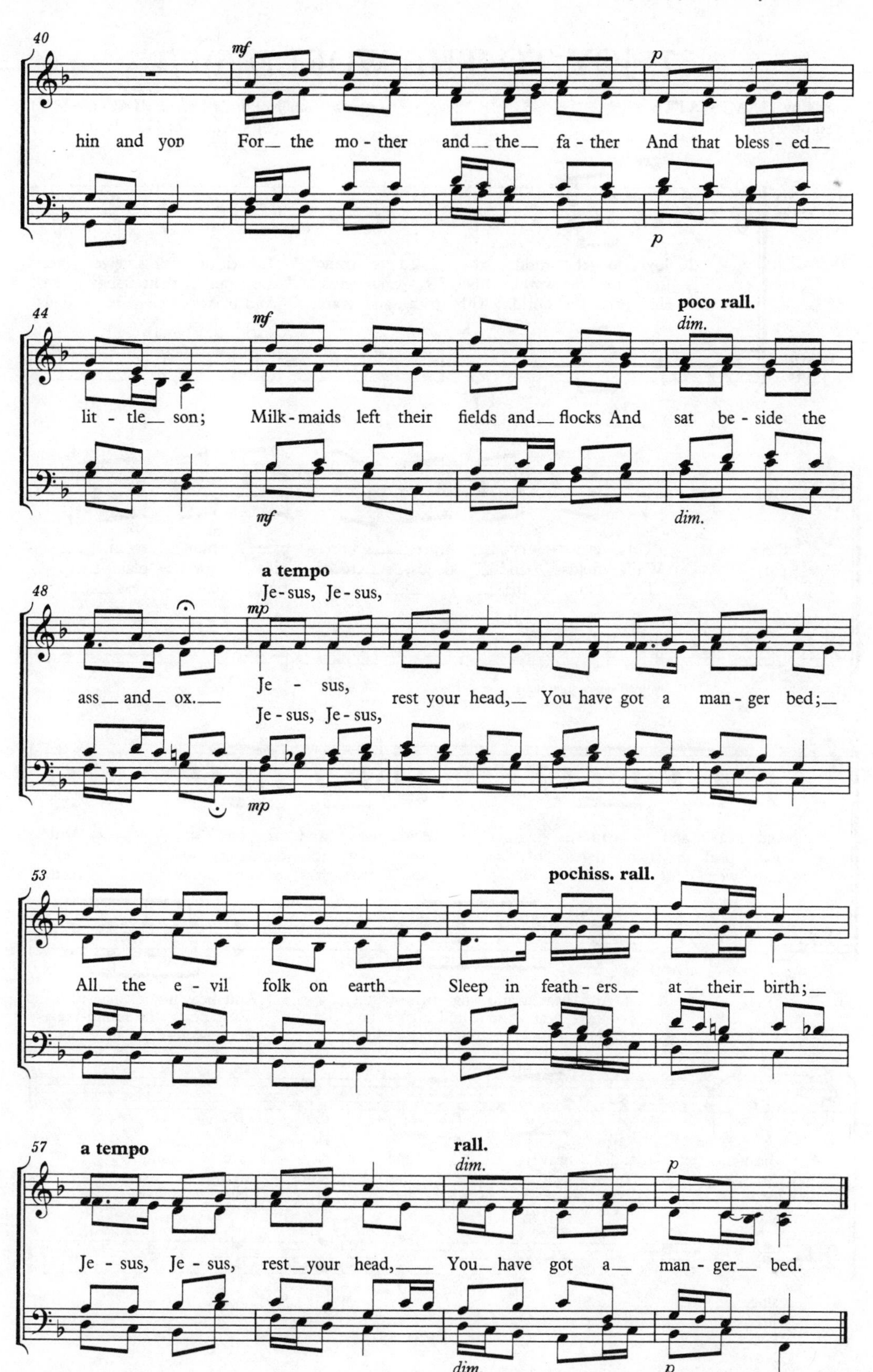
40
mf
p
hin and yon For the mother and the father And that bless-ed
p
44
mf
poco rall.
dim.
lit-tle son; Milk-maids left their fields and flocks And sat be-side the
mf
dim.
48
a tempo
Je-sus, Je-sus,
mp
ass and ox. Je - sus, rest your head, You have got a man-ger bed;
Je-sus, Je-sus,
mp
53
pochiss. rall.
All the e-vil folk on earth Sleep in feath-ers at their birth;
57
a tempo
rall.
dim.
p
Je-sus, Je-sus, rest your head, You have got a man-ger bed.
dim.
p

37. JOY TO THE WORLD (i)

Words by ISAAC WATTS
based on Psalm 98

mostly from Holford's *Voce di Melodia* (*c.*1834)
(with echoes of G.F. HANDEL?)

38. JOY TO THE WORLD (ii)

Words by ISAAC WATTS
based on Psalm 98

mostly from Holford's *Voce di Melodia* (*c.*1834)
(with echoes of G.F. HANDEL?)
arranged by WILLIAM LLEWELLYN

10
-pare him room, And heav'n and na-ture sing, and
And heav'n and na-ture
mf
12
heav'n and na-ture sing, and heav'n, and heav'n and na-ture sing.
sing, and heav'n and na-ture sing,
p
f
15
2. Joy to the world, the
Ped.

18
Sa - viour reigns! Let all their songs em - ploy; While
p
Man.
21
fields_ and_ floods,_ rocks, hills and_ plains_ Re - peat the sound-ing joy, re -
Re-peat the sound-ing
24
- peat the sound-ing joy, re - peat,_ re - peat___ the sound - ing joy.
joy, re - peat the sound-ing joy,
p
f
Ped.

27
3. He rules the world with
Full
Man.
30
truth and grace, And makes the na - tions prove The
33
glo - ries_ of_ his right - eous - ness_ And won - ders of his_ love, and
And won - ders of his
Tpt.

36
won - ders of his love, and won - ders, and won - ders
love, and won - ders of his love,
Full
Ped.
38
of his love.
41
Adagio ♪ = 112
ff
Joy to the world, the Lord is come!
ff
Adagio ♪ = 112
Full ff

for the Middlesex Federation of Women's Institutes

39. KING JESUS HATH A GARDEN

English words by
G. R. WOODWARD

Dutch carol
arranged by WILLIAM LLEWELLYN

* pronounce 'Pay-see-ence'

43
Steady
mf
f
4. The
5. Yet, 'mid the brave, the brav-est prize of all may claim The
mp
49
a tempo
mf
Star of Beth-lem, Je-sus, bles-sed be His Name! There naught is heard But Pa-ra-dise bird, Harp,
p
55
ALL
dul-ci-mer, lute, With cym - bal, Trump and tym-bal, And the ten-der, sooth-ing flute; With
60
cym - bal, Trump and tym-bal, And the ten-der, sooth-ing flute.
mf
mf

65
Slowly
6. Ah! Je-su Lord, my heal and weal, my bliss com - plete, Make thou my heart thy
71
Gently
p ALL
gar-den plot, fair, trim and neat, That I may hear this mu-sick clear: Harp, dul-ci-mer, lute, With
77
cym - bal,— Trump and tym-bal, And the ten-der, sooth-ing flute; With cym - bal,— Trump and tym-bal,
83
ALL
pp
p rall.
And the ten-der, sooth-ing flute. Mm.
ppp

for the Dean, Organist, and Choir of Canterbury Cathedral

40. OUR LADY AND CHILD

Lady, I sing to thee

Words by
VICTOR DE WAAL

PHILIP MOORE

Andante tranquillo ♩ = 72

p **(SOLO** *ad lib.***)**

SOPRANO

1. La - dy, I sing— to thee Ten - der hu -

ORGAN

p

Man.

6

- mi - li - ty, Puzz - ling the grace— In thy Son's face.

12

S. *pp*

A.

(+ Org. *ad lib.*) 2. La - dy that look - est far, Of voy - a - gers— the

T.

B. *pp*

17

the— world's—

star, Thou gav - est sight— To the world's— light.

22
TENORS and BASSES (SOLO ad lib.)
mp
3. Ho - ly La - dy that stood Un - der the cru - el
Org. mp
Ped.
27
rood, That did'st bor - row Thy Son's sor - row.
32
(a few voices) DESCANT ad lib.
S.
mf
4. La - dy, I sing to thee, Crown'd in e -
S. mf
A.
(+Org. ad lib.)
4. La - dy, I sing to thee, Crown'd in e - ter - ni -
T.
B. mf
37
rall.
pp
- ter - ni - ty, Blest in thy Son's face.
pp
thy Son's
- ty, Blest in the grace Of thy Son's face.
pp

41. LULLAY MY LIKING

Words 15th century

GUSTAV HOLST

Words reproduced from *A Medieval Anthology* (Longman)

SOLO
22
3. There was mic - kle me - lo - dy At that child - es birth: Al - though
24
they were in hea - ven's bliss They ma - de mic - kle mirth:

27
REFRAIN
p
Lul - lay my lik - ing, my dear son, my sweet - ing;
p

30
p
pp
Lul - lay my dear heart, mine own dear dar - ling!
p
pp

ALL
33
mf
f
4. An - gels bright they sang that night And said - en to that child 'Bless - ed be
mf
f

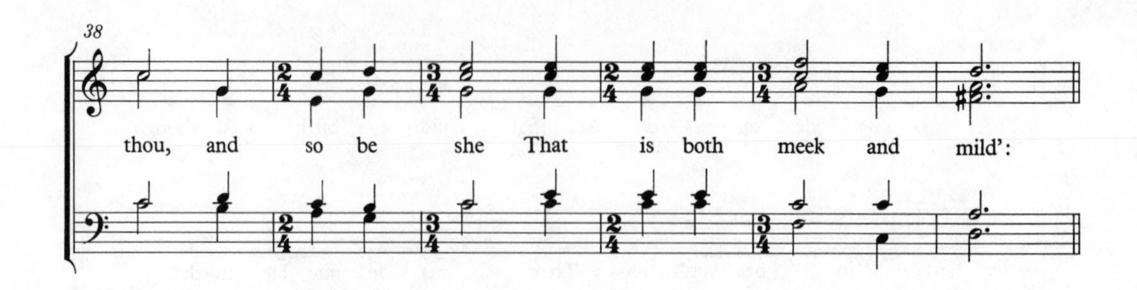
38
thou, and so be she That is both meek and mild':

44 REFRAIN
p
Lul - lay my lik - ing, my dear son, my sweet - ing;
p

47
p
pp
Fine
Lul - lay my dear heart, mine own dear dar - ling!
p
pp

50 SOLO
p
5. Pray we now to that child, And to his mo - ther dear, God
53
D.C. Refrain
grant them all his bless - ing That now mak - en cheer:

42. COVENTRY CAROL (i)

Lully, lulla, thou little tiny child

Words 15th century
from the Coventry Pageant of the Shearmen and Tailors

KENNETH LEIGHTON
Opus 25

No. 2 of *Three Carols* Opus 25

rall. pochiss.
By, by, by, by,
poor young - ling,
marc.
pp
This poor young-ling, For whom we sing, By, by,
poor young - ling,
This poor young-ling,
poco rall.
dim.
più mosso, agitato
lul - ly, lul - lay, lul - ly, lul - lay!
by, by, lul - ly, lul - lay, lul - lay!
He - rod, the king, In his
lul
lay!
ff
ra - - ging,
Charg'd he hath this
In his own sight, All chil - dren young
day His men of might,
In his own sight,
In his own sight, All
In his own sight, All chil - dren

29
S. SOLO
rall.
Tempo I
— to slay,
3. That woe — is me, —
chil - dren young to slay, — to slay, — to
young
33
— woe — is me, Poor child — for thee! — And
slay. — 3. That woe is me, — Poor child for thee! — That
woe — is me, —
37
ev - er morn — and day, For thy part - ing Nor say — nor sing, By, by, by,
marc.
woe — is me, — Poor child — for thee! Lul - ly, lul - la, lul - ly, — lul - la, — lul -
marc.
Lul - ly, — lul - ly, —
41
rall. un poco alla fine
niente
by, lul - ly, lul - lay, — lul - ly, — lul - lay. —
dim. sempre
lul - lay, lul - lay, lul - lay lul - lay.
niente
- ly, lul - ly, lul - lay, — lul - ly, — lul - lay, —
lul - lay, lul - lay.
dim. sempre
lul - lay, — lul - ly, — lul - lay. —
niente
lul - lay. —

for the Linden Singers

43. COVENTRY CAROL (ii)

Lully, lulla, thou little tiny child

Words 15th century
from the Coventry Pageant of the Shearmen and Tailors

Modern version of 16th century English tune
by MARTIN SHAW
arranged by IAN HUMPHRIS

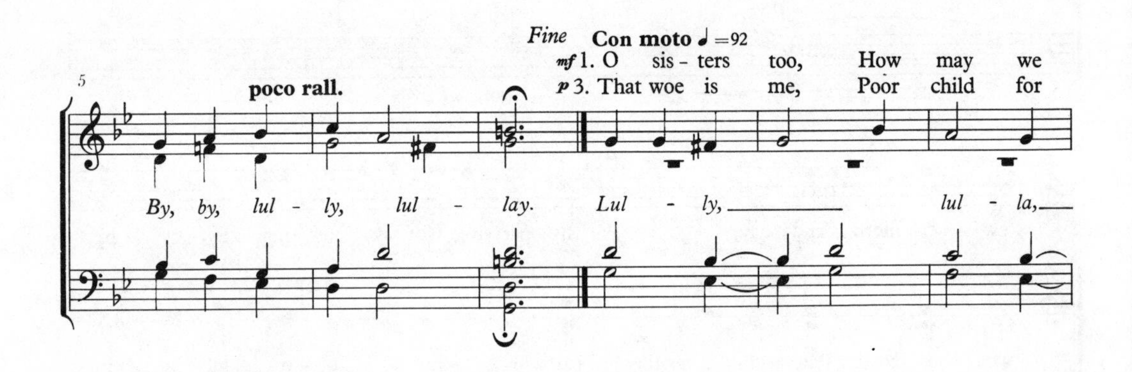

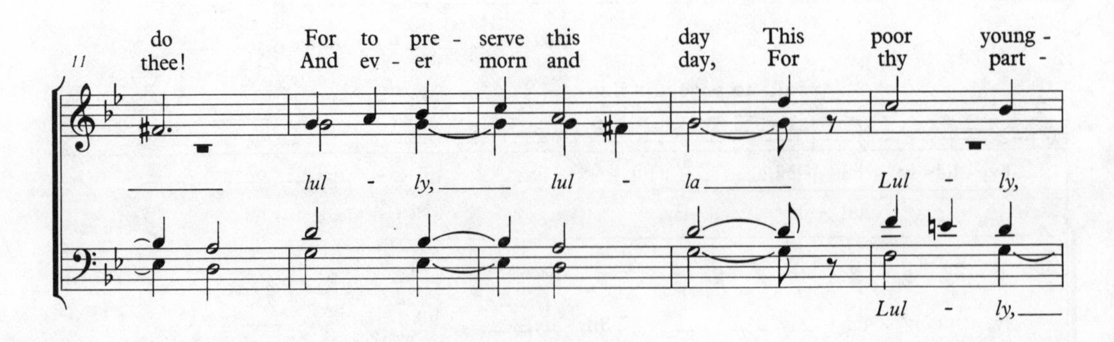

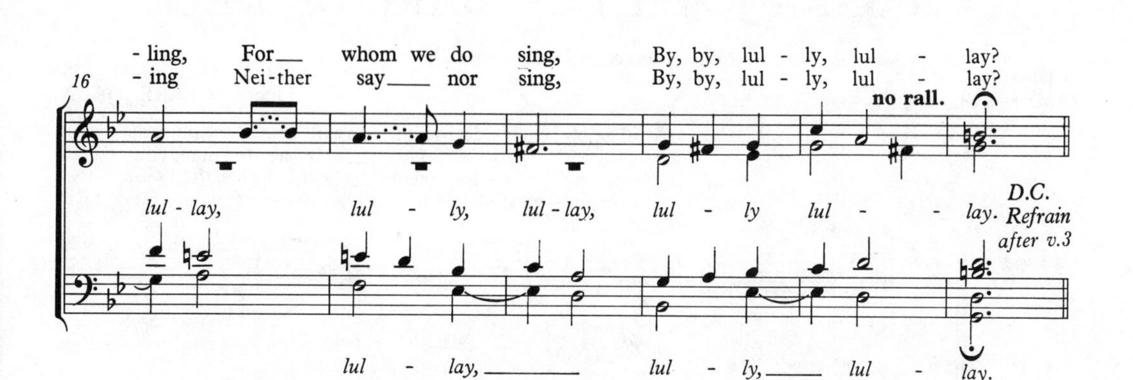
16
- ling, For__ whom we do sing, By, by, lul - ly, lul - lay?
- ing Nei-ther say__ nor sing, By, by, lul - ly, lul - lay?
no rall.
lul - lay, lul - ly, lul - lay, lul - ly lul - lay.
D.C. Refrain after v.3
lul - lay,__ lul - ly,__ lul - lay.

Più moto ♩=96
22
2. He-rod the king, In his ra-ging,
2. He-rod the king, In his__ ra - ging, Char-ged he

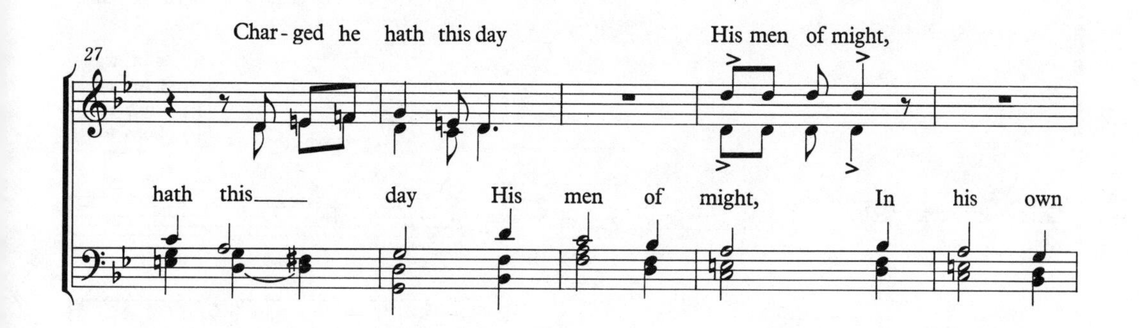
27
Char-ged he hath this day His men of might,
hath this__ day His men of might, In his own

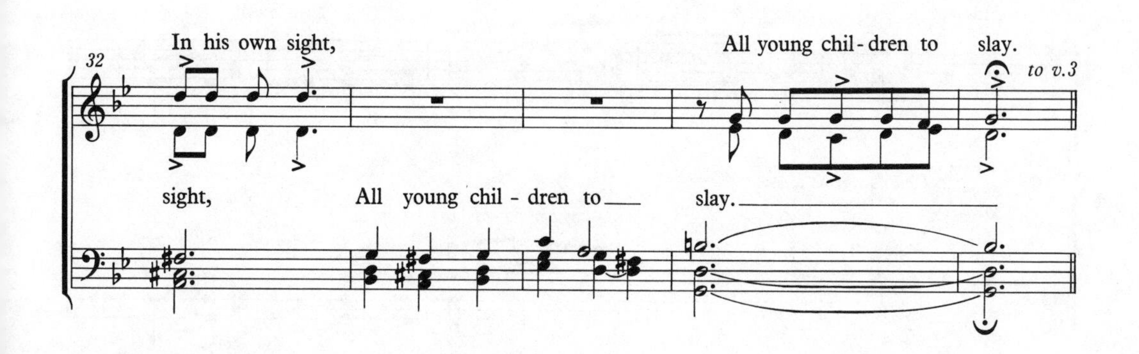
32
In his own sight, All young chil-dren to slay.
to v.3
sight, All young chil - dren to__ slay.__

44a. SANT JOSEP I LA MARE DE DEU

Mary, Mother of God's dear child

English words by
JAMES WOODHOUSE

Traditional Catalan carol
arranged by PERE JORDA

44b. SANT JOSEP I LA MARE DE DEU

45. ROCKING CAROL

Mary's Child, so new and fair

Words by
JAMES WOODHOUSE

Czech carol melody
arranged by WILLIAM LLEWELLYN

* See Performance Notes

Words reproduced by permission of the Author Melody from *The Oxford Book of Carols* by permission of Oxford University Press

9
I
mf
II
mp
-neath her_ ten - der_ care. We will rock thee, Child most ho - ly, Rock thee
la, La-ra la-ra la-ra la, La-ra la-ra la-ra la, La-ra la-ra la-ra la, La-ra la-ra la-ra
La la-ra la, La la-ra la,
mm, mm,
13
I & II
mf
soft - ly, rock thee slow - ly, Rock thee in thy cra - dle_ small, King of_
la, La-ra la-ra la-ra la, La-ra la-ra la-ra la, La-ra la-ra la-ra la, La-ra la-ra la-ra
La la-ra la-ra la, La la - ra la, La, La,
mm, La, la - ra
17
Kings and_Lord of_ all.
la, La-ra la-ra la-ra la, La-ra la-ra la-ra la, La-ra la-ra la-ra la, La-ra la-ra la-ra
mm.
la.

21
SOPRANOS with 1 or 2 TENORS/BARITONES
I mf
II mp
I & II mf
Je - su, Son of God most high, God most high, Low - ly
la, La-ra la-ra la-ra la, La-ra la-ra la-ra la, La-ra la-ra la-ra la, La-ra la-ra la-ra
La-ra la la, La-ra la la, La-ra la la, La-ra la,
La, La, La, La, La, La, La,
25
I mf
II mf
in a sta - ble lie. Do not fear the cat - tle low - ing, Do not
p
mp
la, La-ra la-ra la-ra la, La-ra la-ra la-ra la, La-ra la-ra la-ra la, La-ra la-ra la-ra
La-ra la, La-ra la, La, La la-ra la, La la-ra la,
La, La, La, La, la,
29
I & II
fear the cold wind blow - ing, Sleep thou safe with - in the
f
mf
la, La-ra la-ra la-ra la, La-ra la-ra la-ra la, La-ra la-ra la-ra
La la - ra la, La, la, la, La, la, la,
La, La, La, la, La, la, la,

32
hay, Sweet - ly sleep till break of day.
mp
la, La-ra la-ra la-ra la, La-ra la, La-ra la-ra la la, La-ra la-ra la-ra
La, la, la, la, la-ra la, La.
La, la, la, La.
35
la, La-ra la-ra la-ra la, La-ra la-ra la-ra la, La-ra la-ra la-ra la, La-ra la-ra la-ra
39
pp ppp niente
la, La-ra la-ra la-ra la, mm.

46. MARY WALKED THROUGH A WOOD OF THORN

Old German words
translated by E. HERBORN

PHILIP RADCLIFFE

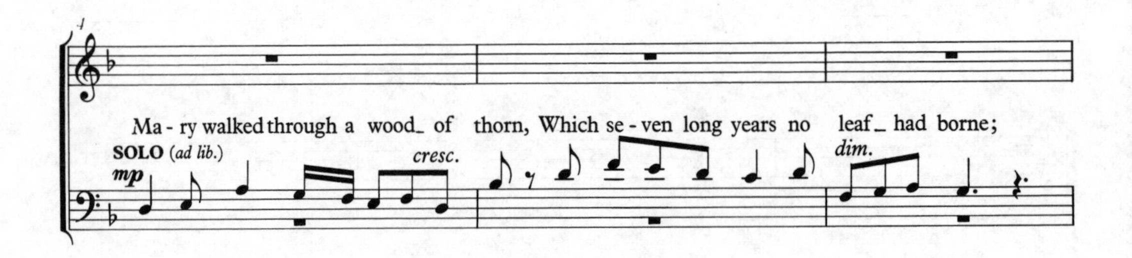

smart Ma - ry bore be - neath her heart,
(FULL)
13
dim.
mf
Je - sus and
mf
16
f
mf
Ma - ry. Then ros - es sprang from out the thorn; Ky - ri - e e -
f
mf
19
cresc.
f
- lei - son. As the Christ - child through the wood was borne, Ros - es sprang from
cresc.
f
22
dim.
out the thorn; Je - sus and Ma - ry.
dim.

47. NOËL NOUVELET (i)

Noel Nouvelet

English words by
MARION JACKSON

Traditional French carol
arranged by STEPHEN JACKSON

26
TENORS
p
2. L'an - ge dis-ait: 'Pas-teurs, par-tez d'i-ci,
2. 'Shep-herds from the fields, let glad-ness fill your mind.
p (strings)
Ped. 16′ only
35
L'â-me en re-pos et le coeur ré-jou-i;
Go to Beth-le-hem, the Lamb of God to find!'
En Beth-lé-em * trou-ver-ez l'ag-ne-let.'
Lo, from the sky the an-gel voi-ces sing
pp
43
pp
No-ël nou-ve-let, No-ël chant-ons i-ci.
'No-el Nou-ve-let' for Christ the newborn King.
Solo p

* Bett-lay-emm

* pronounce 's' in 'tous'

67
S.
A.
T.
B.
Org.
p
p
Ped. 8′ & 16′
mf
(Ped.)
72
S. sf
mf
sfmf
A.
Mm,
mm,
T. sf
mf
sfmf
Mm,
mm,
B.
mf
4. Bien - tôt les rois, par l'é-toile é - clair-cis, De l'O -
4. Soon the three wise men, who by a star were led, Journ-neyed from the
mf
Solo p
(Ped.)
79
sfmf
mm,
sfmf
mm,
-rient dont ils é - taient sor - tis, A Beth - lé - em vin - rent un ma - ti -
East, and at the low-ly bed Each bowed the knee and made an of - fer -

* 'st' not pronounced

105
S. SOLO
(Ah)
Ah,
S.
pp
mp
p
-pli De nous sau-ver par son sang ver-mei-let! No-ël nou-ve-
pain, Bring-ing me heal-ing through Thy suf-fer-ing. 'Noel Nou-ve-
A.
pp
p
-pli De nous sau-ver par son sang ver - meil-let! No -
pain, Bring-ing me heal-ing through Thy suf - fer-ing. 'No -
T.
pp
p
-pli De nous sau-ver par son sang! No -
pain, Bring-ing me heal-ing, heal - ing. 'No -
B.1
pp
p
-pli De nous sau-ver par son sang ver-meil-let! No -
pain, Bring-ing me heal - ing through Thy suf-fer - ing, 'No -
B.2
pp
p
pro-dige ac-com-pli, nous sau-ver par son sang! No - ël
borne my grief and pain, Bring - ing heal - ing, 'No - el
S. SOLO
111
S.
mp
3
-let, No-ël chant-ons i-ci.
-let' for Christ the heaven-ly King.
A.
p mp
poco sf
-ël, No - ël, son sang ver-meil - let!
-el, no - el' the hea - ven-ly King.
T.
p mp
poco sf
-ël, No - ël, son sang ver-meil - let!
-el, no - el' the hea - ven-ly King.
-ël, son sang ver-meil - let!
-el' the hea - ven-ly King.
B.
p mp
poco sf
No - ël, ver-meil - let!
no - el' the hea - ven-ly King.
Solo
mf
mp
Ped. 8' & 16'

118
S.
poco accel.
Tempo I
A.
T.
B.
poco accel.
Tempo I
p
p
f sub. dim.
125 S.
pp
(1.) No-ël nou-ve-let, No-ël chant-ons i - ci. Dé - vo-tes gens, cri-ons à Dieu mer-ci!
(1.)'No-el Nou-ve-let', we sing a new-born King With our earth-ly song the firm-a-ment shall ring.
pp
133
poco cresc.
p
pp sub.
Chant-ons No-ël pour le roi nou-ve-let. No-ël nou-ve-let, No ël chant-ons i - ci.
See how the love of God such joy doth bring.'No-el Nou-ve-let' for Christ the new-born King.
poco cresc.
p
pp sub.
16'off
rit.
a tempo
rall.
142
Ped. 8'only
148
Molto meno mosso
pp possibile
add 16'

for Ashtead Choral Society

48. ALL AND SOME (i)

Nowell sing we

Words 15th century

JEREMY THURLOW

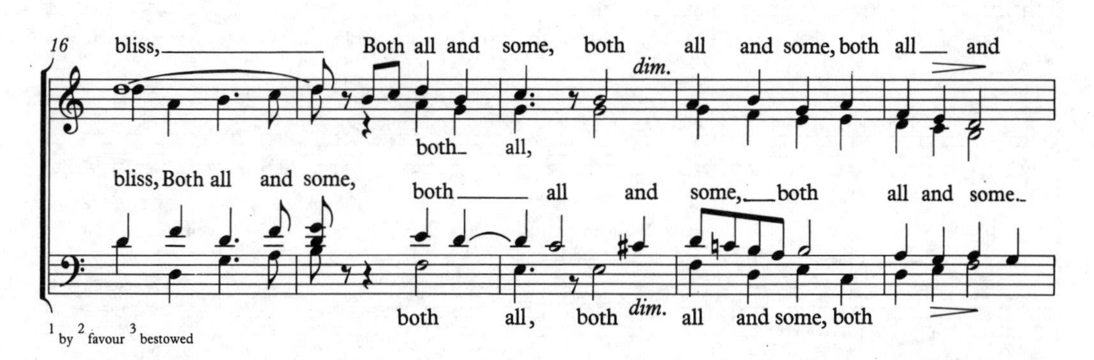

[1] by [2] favour [3] bestowed

21 some. De fruc - tu ven - tris of Ma - ry
p
p
De fruc - tu ven - tris of Ma - ry bright, of Ma - ry bright, Both
p
26
dight:
God and man in her a - light, Out of dis - ease[1] he did us dight:[2] Both all and
31
Both all and some, both all and some, both all and some.
both all
some, both all and some, both all and some, and some.
both all, both all and some, both all and some. Pu - er - na -
f
36
f
Pu - er - na - tus to us was sent, To bliss us bought, fro bale[3] us
Or else to woe
- tus to us was sent, To bliss us bought, fro bale[3] us blent,[4] or else to woe we had y -
41
Both all and some, ff No - well sing we, No -
cresc.
blent,[4] No - well sing we, No - well, No -
ff
- went, else to woe we had y - went, Both all
ff
cresc.
1 misery 2 enforce 3 sorrow 4 turned aside

[1] pitched [2] guide [3] tenure

69
(some)
S.
A.
T.
B.1.
B.2.
mf
mp
No-well sing we,
No-well sing we,
No-well sing we,
No-well sing we,
73
accelerando
ff
Ay! No-well sing we, both all and some, No-well sing
cresc.
76
we, both all and some, No-well sing we, both all and
79
Presto 𝅗𝅥 = 120
some, Now Rex pa-ci-fi-cus is y-come to all and some.

INDEX

ABBREVIATIONS: U=Unaccompanied S=Soprano A=Alto T=Tenor B=Bass Br=Baritone Perc.=Percussion Tp=Timpani

ORCHESTRAL FORCES: Wind (2222)=2 Flutes, 2 Oboes, 2 Clarinets, 2 Bassoons; Brass (2231)=2 Horns, 2 Trumpets, 3 Trombones, 1 Tuba; Tp+2=Timpani+2 further percussion players

NO.	PAGE	U	TITLE AND FIRST LINE (both are shown)	TIME	COMPOSER OR ARRANGER	VOICES Minimum Choir	Solo	INSTRUMENTAL PARTS (on hire) Wind	Brass	Perc.	Strings	JUNIOR BOOK (NJBC)
88	270	U	Canon for three choirs (*Worship the Christ-child*)	1'30"	*W. A. Mozart/W. Ll.*	[SATB]×3						
73	226	U	Carol of the Christ-child (*The Christ-child lay*)	1'30"	*Philip Riley*	SATB						
11	23	U	*Christmas Eve* (The Oxen)	2'30"	*Benjamin Britten*	SA						
9	20	U	*Christmas is coming*	1'40"	*Walford Davies*	SATB						
12	26		*Come all you worthy people here* (A Somerset Carol)	1'30"	*William Llewellyn*	SATB		2222	2231	Tp+2	Strings	NJBC
42	113	U	Coventry Carol (*Lully, lulla*) (i)	2'30"	*Kenneth Leighton*	SATBB	S					
43	116	U	Coventry Carol (*Lully, lulla*) (ii)	2'25"	*Ian Humphris*	SSAATTBB						
8	18	U	Dawn Carol (*Blessed be he that cometh*)	3'15"	*Malcolm Williamson*	SAATTB						
14	30		*De Virgin Mary had a baby boy*	2'20"	*William Llewellyn*	TTBB	Br	2222	2231	Tp+2	Strings	
13	29	U	*Ding-dong, ding*	1'30"	*G. R. Woodward*	SATB						
15	34	U	*Ding dong! merrily on high* (i)	2'10"	*William Llewellyn*	SATB						
16	36	U	*Ding dong! merrily on high* (ii)	2'00"	*H. Le Fèvre Pope*	SSA						NJBC
17	37		*Donkey plod and Mary ride*	4'30"	*Eric Thiman/W. Ll.*	SATB						
18	43	U	*Dormi Jesu* (Our Lady's Lullaby) (i)	0'45"	*Philip Riley*	SSAA						
19	44	U	*Dormi Jesu* (Our Lady's Lullaby) (ii)	1'30"	*Richard R. Bennett*	SSAA						
28b	74	U	El Cant des Ocells (*En veure despuntar*)	3'00"	*Enrique Ribo*	SATB						
83	253	U	El Noi de la Mare (*What shall we give?*)	1'50"	*Enrique Ribo*	SSAATTBB	S					
28b	74	U	*En veure despuntar* (El Cant des Ocells)	3'00"	*Enrique Ribo*	SATB	S					
6	14	U	Fum, fum, fum (*Ancient prophets first foretold him*)	1'10"	*William Llewellyn*	SATTB						NJBC
72	223	U	Gabriel's message (*The angel Gabriel*)	2'15"	*William Llewellyn*	SATB		1200			Strings	NJBC
22	50		*God rest you merry, gentlemen*	2'00"	*William Llewellyn*	SSATBB		2222	2231	Tp+2	Strings	NJBC
20	46		*Hark! the herald angels sing*	3'20"	*Mendelssohn/W. Ll.*	SATB		2222	2231	Tp+2	Strings	NJBC
21	49	U	*Hodie, hodie* (A Fanfare for Christmas)	1'00"	*Robin Wells*	SATB		2222	2231	Tp+2	Strings	
23	57		*How soft, upon the ev'ning air*	1'40"	*Thomas Dunhill/W. Ll.*	SAATTBB		2200			Strings	

82	250	U	Huron Carol (*'Twas in the moon of wintertime*)	1'50"	*William Llewellyn*	SSAATTBB						
24	60	U	*Hushaby low* (Slumber Song of the Madonna)	2'00"	*Ronald Finch*	SAATTBB	S					
25	63	U	*Hush you, my baby*	3'10"	*William Llewellyn*	SSAATTBB	ST					
66	209	U	Il est né, le divin enfant (*See him born*)	2'00"	*William Llewellyn*	SSAATTBB		1200			Strings	NJBC
35	90		Illuminare, Jerusalem (*Jerusalem rejos for joy*)	2'30"	*Judith Weir*	SSAATTBB						
26	66	U	*I'm a-ridin' to Bethlehem* (Troc-a-tron)	0'50"	*Petr Eben*	SATB						
27	68	U	*In dulci jubilo*	3'45"	*R. L. Pearsall*	SATB						
29	76	U	*In the bleak mid-winter* (i)	3'45"	*William Llewellyn*	SATB						
30	80	U	*In the bleak mid-winter* (ii)	3'45"	*Gustav Holst*	SATB		1111			Strings	NJBC
28a	72	U	*In this most joyful night* (The Song of the Birds)	3'00"	*Enrique Ribo*	SATB						
31	81	U	*In thy mother's arms* (Ninna-Nanna)	1'50"	*D. Lavinio Virgili*	SATB		A/Br				
32	84	U	*I saw three ships* (i)	1'00"	*Ian Humphris*	SATB						
33	86	U	*I saw three ships* (ii)	2'05"	*William Llewellyn*	SAATTBB	TB					
34	89	U	*I sing of a maiden*	1'20"	*Robin Wells*	SATTB						
35	90		*Jerusalem rejos for joy* (Illuminare, Jerusalem)	2'30"	*Judith Weir*	SSAATTBB						
36	95	U	*Jesus, Jesus, rest your head*	2'20"	*J. J. Niles/Warrell*	SATB						
86	264	U	Joy shall be yours (*Villagers all, this frosty tide*)	1'30"	*H. Fraser-Simson*	SATB						
37	98	U	*Joy to the World* (i)	1'30"	*? G. F. Handel*	SATB		2222	2231	Tp	Strings	NJBC
38	99		*Joy to the World* (ii)	2'00"	*? G. F. Handel/W. Ll.*	SATB		2222	0200	Tp	Strings	
39	104		*King Jesus hath a garden*	3'05"	*William Llewellyn*	SSAA		2221	2200	Tp+2	Strings	NJBC
40	108		*Lady, I sing to thee* (Our Lady and Child)	1'40"	*Philip Moore*	SSATB						
62	195	U	London Waits (*Past three o'clock*) (i)	2'00"	*Charles Wood*	SATB						NJBC
63	196	U	London Waits (*Past three o'clock*) (ii)	3'00"	*William Llewellyn*	SSAATTBB	Br					
41	110	U	*Lullay my liking*	2'30"	*Gustav Holst*	SATB						
42	113	U	*Lully, lulla* (Coventry Carol) (i)	2'30"	*Kenneth Leighton*	SATBB	S					
43	116	U	*Lully, lulla* (Coventry Carol) (ii)	2'25"	*Ian Humphris*	SSAATTBB						
71	220	U	Lute-book Lullaby (*Sweet was the song the Virgin sang*)	2'15"	*Jeremy Thurlow*	SSAATTBB						

NO.	PAGE	U	TITLE AND FIRST LINE (both are shown)	TIME	COMPOSER OR ARRANGER	VOICES Minimum Choir	Solo	INSTRUMENTAL PARTS (on hire) Wind	Brass	Perc.	Strings	JUNIOR BOOK (NJBC)
44a	118	U	*Mary, Mother of God's dear child* (Sant Josep i la Mare)	1'30"	*Père Jorda*	SATB						
75	229	U	Mary's Child (*Born in the night*)	1'40"	*Geoffrey Ainger/W. Ll.*	SATTBB						NJBC
45	120	U	*Mary's Child, so new and fair* (Rocking Carol)	1'35"	*William Llewellyn*	SAATTBB						NJBC
46	124	U	*Mary walked through a wood of thorn*	1'05"	*Philip Radcliffe*	SATB						
31	81	U	Ninna-Nanna (*In thy mother's arms*)	1'50"	*D. Lavinio Virgili*	SATB	A/Br					
47	126		*Noel Nouvelet* (Noël Nouvelet) (i)	3'20"	*Stephen Jackson*	SSAATTBB	S	2222	2230	Tp+1	Strings	
49	137	U	Noël Nouvelet (*Noel, sing Noel*) (ii)	2'35"	*Ian Humphris*	SATB						
49	137	U	*Noel, sing Noel* (Noël Nouvelet) (ii)	2'35"	*Ian Humphris*	SATB						
50	140	U	*Nowell, Nowell, Who is there?* (Sir Christemas)	1'05"	*Robin Wells*	SATBB						
48	133	U	*Nowell sing we* (All and some) (i)	1'55"	*Jeremy Thurlow*	SSAATTBB		1111	1111	0+3	Strings	
51	142	U	*Nowell sing we* (All and some) (ii)	3'35"	*John Byrt*	SSAATTBB	S					
52	148		*Nowell sing we* (All and some) (iii)	2'40"	*John Joubert*	SATB						
53	156	U	*Now is Christemas ycome* (The Golden Carol)	1'10"	*Paul Bendit*	SSAATTBB						
54	160	U	*Now the holly bears a berry* (Sans Day Carol)	1'50"	*Ian Humphris*	SAATTBB						
55	164	U	*O come, all ye faithful*	4'20"	*William Llewellyn*	SATB		2222	2231	Tp+3	Strings	NJBC
56	168	U	*O leave your sheep*	2'15"	*Ian Humphris*	SATB						
57	170	U	*O magnum misterium*	2'15"	*Giovanni Gabrieli/ W. Ll.*	SATB: TTBB			1210: 1021			
58	183	U	*O my dear heart* (Balulalow) (i)	1'05"	*Richard R. Bennett*	SSSA						
60	186	U	*O my dear heart* (Balulalow) (ii)	1'40"	*Paul Johnson*	SATB						
59	184	U	*Once in royal David's city*	5'30"	*Gauntlett/Mann/Wells*	SATB	S	2222	2231	Tp+3	Strings	NJBC
61	187	U	*On the First day* (The Twelve Days of Christmas)	3'40"	*Ian Humphris*	SSAATTBB	SB					NJBC
40	108		Our Lady and Child (*Lady, I sing to thee*)	1'40"	*Philip Moore*	SSATB						
18	43	U	Our Lady's Lullaby (*Dormi Jesu*) (i)	0'45"	*Philip Riley*	SSAA						
19	44	U	Our Lady's Lullaby (*Dormi Jesu*) (ii)	1'30"	*Richard R. Bennett*	SSAA						

62	195	U	*Past three o'clock* (London Waits) (i)	2'00"	*Charles Wood*	SATB						NJBC
63	196	U	*Past three o'clock* (London Waits) (ii)	3'00"	*William Llewellyn*	SSAATTBB	Br					
85	260		Puer Nobis (*Unto us is born a Son*)	2'00"	*William Llewellyn*	SATB		2222	2231	Tp+2	Strings	NJBC
64	200		*Rejoice and be merry* (A Gallery Carol)	1'30"	*Robin Wells*	SATB		2222	2231	Tp+2	Strings	NJBC
65	204		*Rejoice lordings*	0'50"	*Arthur Oldham*	SATB						
45	120	U	Rocking Carol (*Mary's Child, so new and fair*)	1'35"	*William Llewellyn*	SAATTBB						NJBC
54	160	U	Sans Day Carol (*Now the holly bears a berry*)	1'50"	*Ian Humphris*	SAATTBB						
44a	118	U	Sant Josep i la Mare (*Mary, Mother of God's dear child*)	1'30"	*Père Jorda*	SATB						
44b	119	U	*Sant Josep i la Mare de Deu*	1'30"	*Père Jorda*	SATB						
66	209	U	*See him born* (Il est né, le divin enfant)	2'00"	*William Llewellyn*	SSAATTBB		1200			Strings	NJBC
67	212	U	*See, to us a child is born* (A Christmas Antiphon) (i)	1'30"	*John Wilson*	SATB						
68	213		*See, to us a child is born* (A Christmas Antiphon) (ii)	1'30"	*John Wilson/W. Ll.*	SATB						
69	216	U	*Silent night* (Stille Nacht)	2'40"	*Ian Humphris*	SAATTBB						
70	218	U	*Sing lullaby!* (The Infant King)	1'45"	*William Llewellyn*	SATB						
50	140	U	Sir Christemas (*Nowell, Nowell, Who is there?*)	1'05"	*Robin Wells*	SATBB						
24	60	U	Slumber Song of the Madonna (*Hushaby low*)	2'00"	*Ronald Finch*	SAATTBB	S					
69	216	U	Stille Nacht (*Silent night*)	2'40"	*Ian Humphris*	SAATTBB						
4	6	U	Susanni (*A little child there is yborn*)	1'45"	*Ronald Corp*	SATB						
71	220	U	*Sweet was the song the Virgin sang* (Lute-book Lullaby)	2'15"	*Jeremy Thurlow*	SSAATTBB						
72	223	U	*The angel Gabriel* (Gabriel's message)	2'15"	*William Llewellyn*	SSATTBB		1200			Strings	NJBC
73	226	U	*The Christ-child lay* (Carol of the Christ-child)	1'30"	*Philip Riley*	SATB						
74	228	U	*The first Nowell*	4'30"	*William Llewellyn*	SATB		2222	2231	Tp+2	Strings	NJBC
53	156		The Golden Carol (*Now is Christemas ycome*)	1'10"	*Paul Bendit*	SSAATTBB						
76	234		*The holly and the ivy*	2'45"	*William Llewellyn*	SSAATTBB	ST	2222	2231	Tp+2	Strings	NJBC
70	218	U	The Infant King (*Sing lullaby!*)	1'45"	*William Llewellyn*	SATB						
5	9	U	The little road to Bethlehem (*As I walked down the road*)	3'00"	*Michael Head*	SSAATTBB						
77	236	U	*The oak stands fast* (The Trees of the Field)	1'20"	*David Stone*	SATB						

NO.	PAGE	U	TITLE AND FIRST LINE (both are shown)	TIME	COMPOSER OR ARRANGER	VOICES Minimum Choir	Solo	INSTRUMENTAL PARTS (on hire) Wind	Brass	Perc.	Strings	JUNIOR BOOK (NJBC)
11	23		The Oxen (*Christmas Eve*)	2'30"	*Benjamin Britten*	SA						
78	238	U	*There is no rose of such virtue*	2'00"	*John Joubert*	SATB						
79	240	U	The Shepherds' Farewell (*Thou must leave*)	3'30"	*Hector Berlioz*	SATB		0220			Strings	
28a	72	U	The Song of the Birds (*In this most joyful night*)	3'00"	*Enrique Ribo*	SATB						
77	236	U	The Trees of the Field (*The oak stands fast*)	1'20"	*David Stone*	SATB						
61	187	U	The Twelve Days of Christmas (*On the First day*)	3'40"	*Ian Humphris*	SSAATTBB	SB					NJBC
87	266	U	The Yorkshire Wassail (*Wassail! We've been awhile*)	3'00"	*Ian Humphris*	SSAATTBB	S/A					
79	240	U	*Thou must leave* (The Shepherds' Farewell)	3'30"	*Hector Berlioz*	SATB		0220			Strings	
80	244		*Torches!* (i)	1'40"	*John Joubert*	S or SA		2222	4231	Tp+1	Strings	NJBC
81	247		*Torches!* (ii)	1'40"	*John Joubert*	SATB		2222	4231	Tp+1	Strings	NJBC
26	66	U	Troc-a-tron (*I'm a-ridin' to Bethlehem*)	0'50"	*Petr Eben*	SATB						
82	250	U	*'Twas in the moon of wintertime* (Huron Carol)	1'50"	*William Llewellyn*	SSAATTBB						
84	256	U	*Tyrle, tyrlow*	1'45"	*Healey Willan*	SSAA						
85	260		*Unto us is born a Son* (Puer Nobis)	2'00"	*William Llewellyn*	SATB		2222	2231	Tp+2	Strings	NJBC
86	264	U	*Villagers all, this frosty tide* (Joy shall be yours)	1'30"	*H. Fraser-Simson*	SATB						
87	266	U	*Wassail! We've been awhile* (The Yorkshire Wassail)	3'00"	*Ian Humphris*	SSAATTBB	S/A					
83	253	U	*What shall we give?* (El Noi de la Mare)	1'50"	*Enrique Ribo*	SSAATTBB	S					
89	272	U	*Whence is that goodly fragrance flowing?* (i)	2'15"	*William Llewellyn*	TTBBB	T					
90	274	U	*Whence is that goodly fragrance flowing?* (ii)	2'15"	*Robin Wells*	SSATTBB						
88	270	U	*Worship the Christ-child* (Canon for three choirs)	1'30"	*W. A. Mozart/W. Ll.*	[SATB]×3